MW00637460

questions by

Christa Chapman
Laurie Kagan
Kimberly Vincent
Arthur Lopez

created and designed by
Miguel Kagan

layout by
Miles Richey

illustrated by
Celso Rodriguez

Kagan

© 2005 by ***Kagan Publishing***

This book is published and distributed by ***Kagan Publishing***. All rights are reserved by ***Kagan Publishing.*** No part of this publication may be reproduced or transmitted in any form by any means, electronic or mechanical, including photocopy, recording, or any information storage and retrieval system, without prior written permission from ***Kagan Publishing.*** The blackline masters included in this book may be duplicated only by classroom teachers who purchase the book, and only for use in their own classrooms. To obtain additional copies of this book, other ***Kagan*** publications, or information regarding ***Kagan Publishing*** professional development, contact ***Kagan Publishing.***

Kagan Publishing
981 Calle Amanecer
San Clemente, CA 92673
1 (800) 933-2667
Fax: (949) 545-6301
www.KaganOnline.com

ISBN: 978-1-879097-83-4

Table of Contents

I had six honest serving men
They taught me all I knew:
Their names were Where and What and When and Why and How and Who.

— Rudyard Kipling

Introduction

In your hands you hold a powerful book. It is a member of a series of transformative blackline activity books. Between the covers, you will find questions, questions, and more questions! But these are no ordinary questions. These are the important kind—higher-level thinking questions—the kind that stretch your students' minds; the kind that release your students' natural curiosity about the world; the kind that rack your students' brains; the kind that instill in your students a sense of wonderment about your curriculum.

But we are getting a bit ahead of ourselves. Let's start from the beginning. Since this is a book of questions, it seems only appropriate for this introduction to pose a few questions—about the book and its underlying educational philosophy. So Mr. Kipling's Six Honest Serving Men, if you will, please lead the way:

What?

What are higher-level thinking questions?

This is a loaded question (as should be all good questions). Using our analytic thinking skills, let's break this question down into two smaller questions: 1) What is higher-level thinking? and 2) What are questions? When we understand the types of thinking skills and the types of questions, we can combine the best of both worlds, crafting beautiful questions to generate the range of higher-level thinking in our students!

Types of Thinking

There are many different types of thinking. Some types of thinking include:

- **applying**
- **associating**
- **comparing**
- **contrasting**
- **defining**
- **elaborating**
- **empathizing**
- **experimenting**
- **generalizing**
- **investigating**
- **making analogies**
- **planning**
- **prioritizing**
- **recalling**
- **reflecting**
- **reversing**
- **sequencing**
- **summarizing**
- **synthesizing**
- **assessing**
- **augmenting**
- **connecting**
- **decision-making**
- **drawing conclusions**
- **eliminating**
- **evaluating**
- **explaining**
- **inferring consequences**
- **inventing**
- **memorizing**
- **predicting**
- **problem-solving**
- **reducing**
- **relating**
- **role-taking**
- **substituting**
- **symbolizing**
- **understanding**
- **thinking about thinking (metacognition)**

This is quite a formidable list. It's nowhere near complete. Thinking is a big, multifaceted phenomenon. Perhaps the most widely recognized system for classifying thinking and classroom questions is Benjamin Bloom's Taxonomy of Thinking Skills. Bloom's Taxonomy classifies thinking skills into six hierarchical levels. It begins with the lower levels of thinking skills and moves up to higher-level thinking skills: 1) Knowledge, 2) Comprehension, 3) Application, 4) Analysis, 5) Synthesis, 6) Evaluation. See Bloom's Taxonomy on the following page.

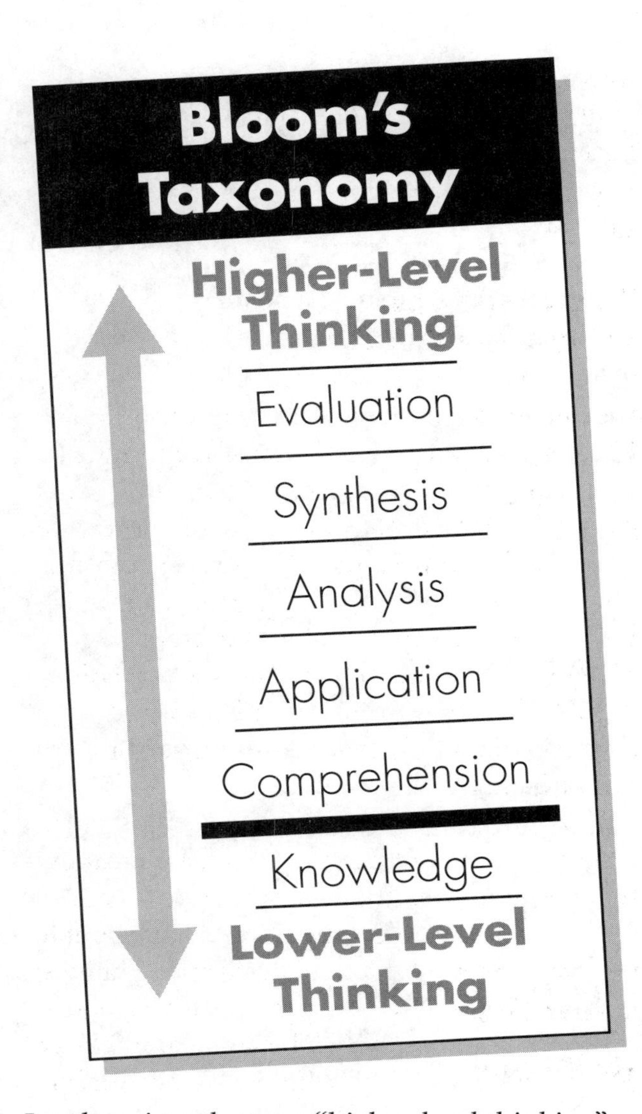

In education, the term "higher-level thinking" often refers to the higher levels of Mr. Bloom's taxonomy. But Bloom's Taxonomy is but one way of organizing and conceptualizing the various types of thinking skills.

There are many ways we can cut the thinking skills pie. We can alternatively view the many different types of thinking skills as, well…many different skills. Some thinking skills may be hierarchical. Some may be interrelated. And some may be relatively independent.

In this book, we take a pragmatic, functional approach. Each type of thinking skill serves a different function. So called "lower-level" thinking skills are very useful for certain purposes. Memorizing and understanding information are invaluable skills that our students will use throughout their lives. But so too are many of the "higher-level" thinking skills on our list. The more facets of students' thinking skills we develop, the better we prepare them for lifelong success.

Because so much classroom learning heretofore has focused on the "lower rungs" of the thinking skills ladder—knowledge and comprehension, or memorization and understanding—in this series of books we have chosen to focus on questions to generate "higher-level" thinking. This book is an attempt to correct the imbalance in the types of thinking skills developed by classroom questions.

Types of Questions

As we ask questions of our students, we further promote cognitive development when we use Fat questions, Low-Consensus questions, and True questions.

Fat Questions vs. Skinny Questions

Skinny questions are questions that require a skinny answer. For example, after reading a poem, we can ask: "Did you like the poem?" Even though this question could be categorized as an Evaluation question—Bloom's highest level of thinking— it can be answered with one monosyllabic word: "Yes" or "No." How much thinking are we actually generating in our students?

We can reframe this question to make it a fat question: "What things did you like about the poem? What things did you dislike?" Notice no short answer will do. Answering this fattened-up question requires more elaboration. These fat questions presuppose not that there is only one thing but things plural that the student liked and things that she did not like. Making things plural is one way to make skinny questions fat. Students stretch their minds to come up with multiple ideas or solutions. Other easy ways to make questions fat is to add "Why or why not?" or "Explain" or "Describe" or "Defend your position" to the end of a question. These additions promote elaboration beyond a skinny answer. Because language and thought are intimately intertwined, questions that require elaborate responses stretch students' thinking: They grapple to articulate their thoughts.

The type of questions we ask impact not just the type of thinking we develop in our students, but also the depth of thought. Fat questions elicit fat responses. Fat responses develop both depth of thinking and range of thinking skills. The questions in this book are designed to elicit fat responses—deep and varied thinking.

High-Consensus Questions vs. Low-Consensus Questions

A high-consensus question is one to which most people would give the same response, usually a right or wrong answer. After learning about sound, we can ask our students: "What is the name of a room specially designed to improve acoustics for the audience?" This is a high-consensus question. The answer (auditorium) is either correct or incorrect.

Education is not the filling of a pail, but the lighting of a fire.

— William Butler Yeats

Compare the previous question with a low-consensus question: "If you were going to build an auditorium, what special design features would you take into consideration?" Notice, to the low-consensus question there is no right or wrong answer. Each person formulates his or her unique response. To answer, students must apply what they learned, use their ingenuity and creativity.

High-consensus questions promote convergent thinking. With high-consensus questions we strive to direct students ***what to think***. Low-consensus questions promote divergent thinking, both critical and creative. With low-consensus questions we strive to develop students' ***ability to think***. The questions in this book are low-consensus questions designed to promote independent, critical and creative thought.

True Questions vs. Review Questions

We all know what review questions are. They're the ones in the back of every chapter and unit. Review questions ask students to regurgitate previously stated or learned information. For example, after learning about the rain forest we may ask: "What percent of the world's oxygen does the rain forest produce?" Students can go back a few pages in their books or into their memory banks and pull out the answer. This is great if we are working on memorization skills, but does little to develop "higher-order" thinking skills.

True questions, on the other hand, are meaningful questions—questions to which we do not know the answer. For example: "What might happen if all the world's rain forests were cut down?" This is a hypothetical; we don't know the answer but considering the question forces us to think. We infer some logical consequences based on what we know. The goal of true questions is not a correct answer, but the thinking journey students take to create a meaningful response. True questions are more representative of real life. Seldom is there a black and white answer. In life, we struggle with ambiguity, confounding variables, and uncertain outcomes. There are millions of shades of gray. True questions prepare students to deal with life's uncertainties.

When we ask a review question, we know the answer and are checking to see if the student does also. When we ask a true question, it is truly a question. We don't necessarily know the answer

Types of Questions

Skinny →	**Fat**
• Short Answer • Shallow Thinking	• Elaborated Answer • Deep Thinking
High-Consensus →	**Low-Consensus**
• Right or Wrong Answer • Develops Convergent Thinking • "What" to Think	• No Single Correct Answer • Develops Divergent Thinking • "How" to Think
Review →	**True**
• Asker Knows Answer • Checking for Correctness	• Asker Doesn't Know Answer • Invitation to Think

and neither does the student. True questions are often an invitation to think, ponder, speculate, and engage in a questioning process.

We can use true questions in the classroom to make our curriculum more personally meaningful, to promote investigation, and awaken students' sense of awe and wonderment in what we teach. Many questions you will find in this book are true questions designed to make the content provocative, intriguing, and personally relevant.

The box above summarizes the different types of questions. The questions you will find in this book are a move away from skinny, high-consensus, review questions toward fat, low-consensus true questions. As we ask these types of questions in our class, we transform even mundane content into a springboard for higher-level thinking. As we integrate these question gems into our daily lessons, we create powerful learning experiences. ***We do not fill our students' pails with knowledge; we kindle their fires to become lifetime thinkers.***

Why?

Why should I use higher-level thinking questions in my classroom?

As we enter the new millennium, major shifts in our economic structure are changing the ways we work and live. The direction is increasingly toward an information-based, high-tech economy. The sum of our technological information is exploding. We could give you a figure how rapidly information is doubling, but by the time you read this, the number would be outdated! No kidding.

But this is no surprise. This is our daily reality. We see it around us everyday and on the news: cloning, gene manipulation, e-mail, the Internet, Mars rovers, electric cars, hybrids, laser surgery, CD-ROMs, DVDs. All around us we see the wheels of progress turning: New discoveries, new technologies, a new societal knowledge and information base. New jobs are being created today in fields that simply didn't exist yesterday.

How do we best prepare our students for this uncertain future—a future in which the only constant will be change? As we are propelled into a world of ever-increasing change, what is the relative value of teaching students facts versus thinking skills? This point becomes even more salient when we realize that students cannot master everything, and many facts will soon become obsolete. Facts become outdated or irrelevant. Thinking skills are for a lifetime. Increasingly, how we define educational success will be away from the quantity of information mastered. Instead, we will define success as our students' ability to generate questions, apply, synthesize, predict, evaluate, compare, categorize.

Virtually the only predictable trend is continuing change.

— Dr. Linda Tsantis, Creating the Future

If we as a professionals are to proactively respond to these societal shifts, thinking skills will become central to our curriculum. Whether we teach thinking skills directly, or we integrate them into our curriculum, the power to think is the greatest gift we can give our students!

We believe the questions you will find in this book are a step in the direction of preparing students for lifelong success. The goal is to develop independent thinkers who are critical and creative, regardless of the content. We hope the books in this series are more than sets of questions. We provide them as a model approach to questioning in the classroom.

On pages 8 and 9, you will find Questions to Engage Students' Thinking Skills. These pages contain numerous types of thinking and questions designed to engage each thinking skill. As you make your own questions for your students with your own content, use these question starters to help you frame your questions to stimulate various facets of your students' thinking skills. Also let your students use these question starters to generate their own higher-level thinking questions about the curriculum.

Who?

Who is this book for?

This book is for you and your students, but mostly for your students. It is designed to help make your job easier. Inside you will find hundreds of ready-to-use reproducible questions. Sometimes in the press for time we opt for what is easy over what is best. These books attempt to make easy what is best. In this treasure chest, you will find hours and hours of timesaving ready-made questions and activities.

Place Higher-Level Thinking In Your Students' Hands

As previously mentioned, this book is even more for your students than for you. As teachers, we ask a tremendous number of questions. Primary teachers ask 3.5 to 6.5 questions per minute! Elementary teachers average 348 questions a day. How many questions would you predict our students ask? Researchers asked this question. What they found was shocking: Typical students ask approximately one question per month.* One question per month!

Although this study may not be representative of your classroom, it does suggest that in general, as teachers we are missing out on a very powerful force—student-generated questions. The capacity to answer higher-level thinking

* Myra & David Sadker, "Questioning Skills" in *Classroom Teaching Skills*, 2nd ed. Lexington, MA: D.C. Heath & Co., 1982.

Questions to Engage Students' Thinking Skills

Analyzing
- How could you break down...?
- What components...?
- What qualities/characteristics...?

Applying
- How is ____ an example of...?
- What practical applications...?
- What examples...?
- How could you use...?
- How does this apply to...?
- In your life, how would you apply...?

Assessing
- By what criteria would you assess...?
- What grade would you give...?
- How could you improve...?

Augmenting/Elaborating
- What ideas might you add to...?
- What more can you say about...?

Categorizing/Classifying/Organizing
- How might you classify...?
- If you were going to categorize...?

Comparing/Contrasting
- How would you compare...?
- What similarities...?
- What are the differences between...?
- How is ____ different...?

Connecting/Associating
- What do you already know about...?
- What connections can you make between...?
- What things do you think of when you think of...?

Decision-Making
- How would you decide...?
- If you had to choose between...?

Defining
- How would you define...?
- In your own words, what is...?

Describing/Summarizing
- How could you describe/summarize...?
- If you were a reporter, how would you describe...?

Determining Cause/Effect
- What is the cause of...?
- How does ____ effect ____?
- What impact might...?

Drawing Conclusions/ Inferring Consequences
- What conclusions can you draw from...?
- What would happen if...?
- What would have happened if...?
- If you changed ____, what might happen?

Eliminating
- What part of ____ might you eliminate?
- How could you get rid of...?

Evaluating
- What is your opinion about...?
- Do you prefer...?
- Would you rather...?
- What is your favorite...?
- Do you agree or disagree...?
- What are the positive and negative aspects of...?
- What are the advantages and disadvantages...?
- If you were a judge...?
- On a scale of 1 to 10, how would you rate...?
- What is the most important...?
- Is it better or worse...?

Explaining
- How can you explain...?
- What factors might explain...?

Experimenting
- How could you test...?
- What experiment could you do to...?

Generalizing
- What general rule can...?
- What principle could you apply...?
- What can you say about all...?

Interpreting
- Why is ____ important?
- What is the significance of...?
- What role...?
- What is the moral of...?

Inventing
- What could you invent to...?
- What machine could...?

Investigating
- How could you find out more about...?
- If you wanted to know about...?

Making Analogies
- How is ____ like ____?
- What analogy can you invent for...?

Observing
- What observations did you make about...?
- What changes...?

Patterning
- What patterns can you find...?
- How would you describe the organization of...?

Planning
- What preparations would you...?

Predicting/Hypothesizing
- What would you predict...?
- What is your theory about...?
- If you were going to guess...?

Prioritizing
- What is more important...?
- How might you prioritize...?

Problem-Solving
- How would you approach the problem?
- What are some possible solutions to...?

Reducing/Simplifying
- In a word, how would you describe...?
- How can you simplify...?

Reflecting/Metacognition
- What would you think if...?
- How can you describe what you were thinking when...?

Relating
- How is ____ related to ____?
- What is the relationship between...?
- How does ____ depend on ____?

Reversing/Inversing
- What is the opposite of...?

Role-Taking/Empathizing
- If you were (someone/something else)...?
- How would you feel if...?

Sequencing
- How could you sequence...?
- What steps are involved in...?

Substituting
- What could have been used instead of...?
- What else could you use for...?
- What might you substitute for...?
- What is another way...?

Symbolizing
- How could you draw...?
- What symbol best represents...?

Synthesizing
- How could you combine...?
- What could you put together...?

questions is a wonderful skill we can give our students, as is the skill to solve problems. Arguably more important skills are the ability to find problems to solve and formulate questions to answer. If we look at the great thinkers of the world—the Einsteins, the Edisons, the Freuds—their thinking is marked by a yearning to solve tremendous questions and problems. It is this questioning process that distinguishes those who illuminate and create our world from those who merely accept it.

Asking a good question requires students to think harder than giving a good answer.

— Robert Fisher, Teaching Children to Learn

Make Learning an Interactive Process

Higher-level thinking is not just something that occurs between students' ears! Students benefit from an interactive process. This basic premise underlies the majority of activities you will find in this book.

As students discuss questions and listen to others, they are confronted with differing perspectives and are pushed to articulate their own thinking well beyond the level they could attain on their own. Students too have an enormous capacity to mediate each other's learning. When we heterogeneously group students to work together, we create an environment to move students through their zone of proximal development. We also provide opportunities for tutoring and leadership. Verbal interaction with peers in cooperative groups adds a dimension to questions not available with whole-class questions and answers.

Reflect on this analogy: If we wanted to teach our students to catch and throw, we could bring in one tennis ball and take turns throwing it to each student and having them throw it back to us. Alternatively, we could bring in twenty balls and have our students form small groups and have them toss the ball back and forth to each other. Picture the two classrooms: One with twenty balls being caught at any one moment, and the other with just one. In which class would students better and more quickly learn to catch and throw?

The same is true with thinking skills. When we make our students more active participants in the learning process, they are given dramatically more opportunities to produce their own thought and to strengthen their own thinking skills. Would you rather have one question being asked and answered at any one moment in your class, or twenty? Small groups mean more questioning and more thinking. Instead of rarely answering a teacher question or rarely generating their own question, asking and answering questions becomes a regular part of your students' day. It is through cooperative interaction that we truly turn our classroom into a higher-level think tank. The associated personal and social benefits are invaluable.

When? When do I use higher-level thinking questions?

Do I use these questions at the beginning of the lesson, during the lesson, or after? The answer, of course, is all of the above.

Use these questions or your own thinking questions at the beginning of the lesson to provide a motivational set for the lesson. Pique students' interest about the content with some provocative questions: "What would happen if we didn't have gravity?" "Why did Pilgrims get along with some Native Americans, but not others?" "What do you think this book will be about?" Make the content personally relevant by bringing in students' own knowledge, experiences, and feelings about the content: "What do you know about spiders?" "What things do you like about mystery stories?" "How would you feel if explorers invaded your land and killed your family?" "What do you wonder about electricity?"

Use the higher-level thinking questions throughout your lessons. Use the many questions and activities in this book not as a replacement of your curriculum, but as an additional avenue to explore the content and stretch students' thinking skills.

Use the questions after your lesson. Use the higher-level thinking questions, a journal writing activity, or the question starters as an extension activity to your lesson or unit.

Or just use the questions as stand-alone sponge activities for students or teams who have finished their work and need a challenging project to work on.

It doesn't matter when you use them, just use them frequently. As questioning becomes a habitual part of the classroom day, students' fear of asking silly questions is diminished. As the ancient Chinese proverb states, "Those who ask a silly question may seem a fool for five minutes, but those who do not ask remain a fool for life."

The important thing is to never stop questioning.

— Albert Einstein

As teachers, we should make a conscious effort to ensure that a portion of the many questions we ask on a daily basis are those that move our students beyond rote memorization. When we integrate higher-level thinking questions into our daily lessons, we transform our role from transmitters of knowledge to engineers of learning.

Where? Where should I keep this book?

Keep it close by. Inside there are 25 sets of questions. Pull it out any time you teach these topics or need a quick, easy, fun activity or journal writing topic.

How? How do I get the most out of this book?

In this book you will find 16 topics arranged alphabetically. For each topic there are reproducible pages for: 1) 16 Question Cards, and 2) a Journal Writing activity page.

1. Question Cards

The Question Cards are truly the heart of this book. There are numerous ways the Question Cards can be used. After the other activity pages are introduced, you will find a description of a variety of engaging formats to use the Question Cards.

Especies en Peligro de Extinción
Question Cards

Especies en Peligro de Extinción
1 ¿De qué forma la economía de un lugar pone en peligro de extinción a sus animales?

Especies en Peligro de Extinción
2 ¿Qué puede hacer la gente para proteger a las especies en peligro de extinción que viven en su área o en otros continentes?

Especies en Peligro de Extinción
3 Si se siguen destruyendo las selvas tropicales, ¿cuáles son los posibles efectos en todo el mundo?

Especies en Peligro de Extinción
4 El uso de insecticidas afecta a la población de aves. ¿Cómo afecta esto, a su vez, a la población humana?

Higher-Level Thinking Questions for Spanish
Kagan Publishing • 1 (800) 933-2667 • www.KaganOnline.com 143

Specific and General Questions

Some of the questions provided in this book series are content-specific and others are content-free. For example, the literature questions in the Literature books are content-specific. Questions for the Great Kapok Tree deal specifically with that literature selection. Some language arts questions in the Language Arts book, on the other hand, are content-free. They are general questions that can be used over and over again with new content. For example, the Book Review questions can be used after reading any book. The Story Structure questions can be used after reading any story. You can tell by glancing at the title of the set and some of the questions whether the set is content-specific or content-free.

A Little Disclaimer

Not all of the "questions" on the Question Cards are actually questions. Some instruct students to do something. For example, "Compare and contrast…" We can also use these directives to develop the various facets of students' thinking skills.

The Power of Think Time

As you and your students use these questions, don't forget about the power of Think Time! There are two different think times. The first is the time between the question and the response. The second is the time between the response and feedback on the response. Think time has been shown to greatly enhance the quality of student thinking. If students are not pausing for either think time, or doing it too briefly, emphasize its importance. Five little seconds of silent think time after the question and five more seconds before feedback are proven, powerful ways to promote higher-level thinking in your class.

Use Your Question Cards for Years

For attractive Question Cards that will last for years, photocopy them on color card-stock paper and laminate them. To save time, have the Materials Monitor from each team pick up one card set, a pair of scissors for the team, and an envelope or rubber band. Each team cuts out their own set of Question Cards. When they are done with the activity, students can place the Question Cards in the envelope and write the name of the set on the envelope or wrap the cards with a rubber band for storage.

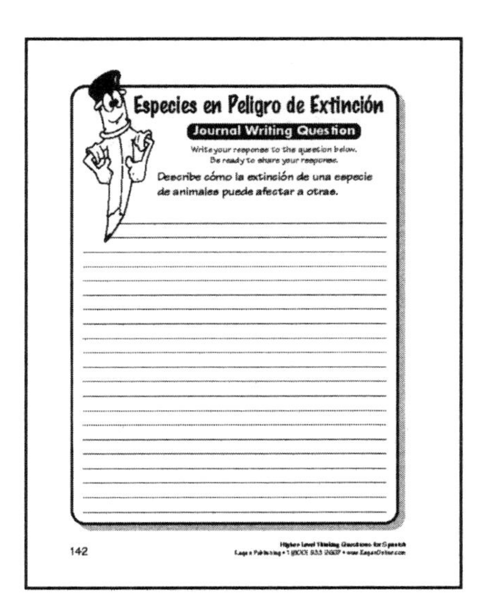

Especies en Peligro de Extinción

Journal Writing Question

Write your response to the question below.
Be ready to share your response.

Describe cómo la extinción de una especie de animales puede afectar a otras.

142

2. Journal Question

The Journal Writing page contains one of the 16 questions as a journal writing prompt. You can substitute any question, or use one of your own. The power of journal writing cannot be overstated. The act of writing takes longer than speaking and thinking. It allows the brain time to make deep connections to the content. Writing requires the writer to present his or her response in a clear, concise language. Writing develops both strong thinking and communication skills.

A helpful activity before journal writing is to have students discuss the question in pairs or in small teams. Students discuss their ideas and what they plan to write. This little prewriting activity ignites ideas for those students who stare blankly at their Journal Writing page. The interpersonal interaction further helps students articulate what they are thinking about the topic and invites students to delve deeper into the topic.

Tell students before they write that they will share their journal entries with a partner or with their team. This motivates many students to improve their entry. Sharing written responses also promotes flexible thinking with open-ended questions, and allows students to hear their peers' responses, ideas and writing styles.

Have students keep a collection of their journal entries in a three-ring binder. This way you can collect them if you wish for assessment or have students go back to reflect on their own learning. If you are using questions across the curriculum, each subject can have its own journal or own section within the binder. Use the provided blackline on the following page for a cover for students' journals or have students design their own.

JOURNAL

My Best Thinking

This Journal Belongs to

Table of Activities

The Question Cards can be used in a variety of game-like formats to forge students' thinking skills. They can be used for cooperative team and pair work, for whole-class questioning, for independent activities, or at learning centers. On the following pages you will find numerous excellent options to use your Question Cards. As you use the Question Cards in this book, try the different activities listed below to add novelty and variety to the higher-level thinking process.

Team Activities

Class Activities

Pair Activities

Individual Activities

Learning Centers

Higher-Level Thinking Question Card

Activities

team activity #1

Question Commander

Preferably in teams of four, students shuffle their Question Cards and place them in a stack, questions facing down, so that all teammates can easily reach the Question Cards. Give each team a Question Commander set of instructions (blackline provided on following page) to lead them through each question.

Student One becomes the Question Commander for the first question. The Question Commander reads the question aloud to the team, then asks the teammates to think about the question and how they would answer it. After the think time, the Question Commander selects a teammate to answer the question. The Question Commander can spin a spinner or roll a die to select who will answer. After the teammate gives the answer, Question Commander again calls for think time, this time asking the team to think about the answer. After the think time, the Question Commander leads a team discussion in which any teammember can contribute his or her thoughts or ideas to the question, or give praise or reactions to the answer.

When the discussion is over, Student Two becomes the Question Commander for the next question.

Question Commander

Instruction Cards

Question Commander

1. Ask the Question: Question Commander reads the question to the team.
2. Think Time: "Think of your best answer."
3. Answer the Question: The Question Commander selects a teammate to answer the question.
4. Think Time: "Think about how you would answer differently or add to the answer."
5. Team Discussion: As a team, discuss other possible answers or reactions to the answer given.

Question Commander

1. Ask the Question: Question Commander reads the question to the team.
2. Think Time: "Think of your best answer."
3. Answer the Question: The Question Commander selects a teammate to answer the question.
4. Think Time: "Think about how you would answer differently or add to the answer."
5. Team Discussion: As a team, discuss other possible answers or reactions to the answer given.

Question Commander

1. Ask the Question: Question Commander reads the question to the team.
2. Think Time: "Think of your best answer."
3. Answer the Question: The Question Commander selects a teammate to answer the question.
4. Think Time: "Think about how you would answer differently or add to the answer."
5. Team Discussion: As a team, discuss other possible answers or reactions to the answer given.

Question Commander

1. Ask the Question: Question Commander reads the question to the team.
2. Think Time: "Think of your best answer."
3. Answer the Question: The Question Commander selects a teammate to answer the question.
4. Think Time: "Think about how you would answer differently or add to the answer."
5. Team Discussion: As a team, discuss other possible answers or reactions to the answer given.

team activity #2

Fan-N-Pick

In a team of four, Student One fans out the question cards, and says, "Pick a card, any card!" Student Two picks a card and reads the question out loud to teammates. After five seconds of think time, Student Three gives his or her answer. After another five seconds of think time, Student Four paraphrases, praises, or adds to the answer given. Students rotate roles for each new

team activity #3

Spin-N-Think

Spin-N-Think spinners are available from Kagan to lead teams through the steps of higher-level thinking. Students spin the Spin-N-Think™ spinner to select a student at each stage of the questioning to: 1) ask the question, 2) answer the question, 3) paraphrase and praise the answer, 4) augment the answer, and 5) discuss the question or answer. The Spin-N-Think™ game makes higher-level thinking more fun, and holds students accountable because they are often called upon, but never know when their number will come up.

team activity #4

Three-Step Interview

After the question is read to the team, students pair up. The first step is an interview in which one student interviews the other about the question. In the second step, students remain with their partner but switch roles: The interviewer becomes the interviewee. In the third step, the pairs come back together and each student in turn presents to the team what their partner shared. Three-Step Interview is strong for individual accountability, active listening, and paraphrasing skills.

team activity #5

Team Discussion

Team Discussion is an easy and informal way of processing the questions: Students read a question and then throw it open for discussion. Team Discussion, however, does not ensure that there is individual accountability or equal participation.

team activity #6

Think-Pair-Square

One student reads a question out loud to teammates. Partners on the same side of the table then pair up to discuss the question and their answers. Then, all four students come together for an open discussion about the question.

team activity #7

Question-Write-RoundRobin

Students take turns asking the team the question. After each question is asked, each student writes his or her ideas on a piece of paper. After students have finished writing, in turn they share their ideas. This format creates strong individual accountability because each student is expected to develop and share an answer for every question.

class activity #1

Mix-Pair-Discuss

Each student gets a different Question Card. For 16 to 32 students, use two sets of questions. In this case, some students may have the same question which is OK. Students get out of their seats and mix around the classroom. They pair up with a partner. One partner reads his or her Question Card and the other answers. Then they switch roles. When done they trade cards and find a new partner. The process is repeated for a predetermined amount of time. The rule is students cannot pair up with the same partner twice. Students may get the same questions twice or more, but each time it is with a new partner. This strategy is a fun, energizing way to ask and answer questions.

class activity #2

Think-Pair-Share

Think-Pair-Share is teacher-directed. The teacher asks the question, then gives students think time. Students then pair up to share their thoughts about the question. After the pair discussion, one student is called on to share with the class what was shared in his or her pair. Think-Pair-Share does not provide as much active participation for students as Think-Pair-Square because only one student is called upon at a time, but is a nice way to do whole-class sharing.

class activity #3

Inside-Outside Circle

Each student gets a Question Card. Half of the students form a circle facing out. The other half forms a circle around the inside circle; each student in the outside circle faces one student in the inside circle. Students in the outside circle ask inside circle students a question. After the inside circle students answer the question, students switch roles questioning and answering. After both have asked and answered a question, they each praise theother's answers and then hold up a hand indicating they are finished. When most students have a hand up, have students trade cards with their partner and rotate to a new partner. To rotate, tell the outside circle to move to the left. This format is a lively and enjoyable way to ask questions and have students listen to the thinking of many classmates.

class activity #4

Question & Answer

This might sound familiar: Instead of giving students the Question Cards, the teacher asks the questions and calls on one student at a time to answer. This traditional format eliminates simultaneous, cooperative interaction, but may be good for introducing younger students to higher-level questions.

class activity #5

Numbered Heads Together

Students number off in their teams so that every student has a number. The teacher asks a question. Students put their "heads together" to discuss the question. The teacher then calls on a number and selects a student with that number to share what his or her team discussed.

pair activity #1

RallyRobin

Each pair gets a set of Question Cards. Student A in the pair reads the question out loud to his or her partner. Student B answers. Partners take turns asking and answering each question.

pair activity #2

Pair Discussion

Partners take turns asking the question. The pair then discusses the answer together. Unlike RallyRobin, students discuss the answer. Both students contribute to answering and to discussing each other's ideas.

pair activity #3

Question-Write-Share-Discuss

One partner reads the Question Card out loud to his or her teammate. Both students write down their ideas. Partners take turns sharing what they wrote. Partners discuss how their ideas are similar and different.

individual activity #1

Journal Writing

Students pick one Question Card and make a journal entry or use the question as the prompt for an essay or creative writing. Have students share their writing with a partner or in turn with teammates.

individual activity #2

Independent Answers

Students each get their own set of Questions Cards. Pairs or teams can share a set of questions, or the questions can be written on the board or put on the overhead projector. Students work by themselves to answer the questions on a separate sheet of paper. When done, students can compare their answers with a partner, teammates, or the whole class.

Center Ideas

1. Question Card Center

At one center, have the Question Cards and a Spin-N-Think™ spinner, Question Commander instruction card, or Fan-N-Pick instructions. Students lead themselves through the thinking questions. For individual accountability, have each student record their own answer for each question.

2. Journal Writing Center

At a second center, have a Journal Writing activity page for each student. Students can discuss the question with others at their center, then write their own journal entry. After everyone is done writing, students share what they wrote with other students at their center.

3. Question Starters Center

At a third center, have a Question Starters page. Split the students at the center into two groups. Have both groups create thinking questions using the Question Starters activity page. When the groups are done writing their questions, they trade questions with the other group at their center. When done answering each other's questions, two groups pair up to compare their answers.

Cuentos de Aventuras

Adventure Stories

higher-level thinking questions

Cuentos de Aventuras

Journal Writing Question

Write your response to the question below.
Be ready to share your response.

¿Qué cambios harías en el cuento si tuviera lugar en la antigüedad o en el futuro?

Cuentos de Aventuras
Question Cards

Cuentos de Aventuras

1 ¿Hay animales en el cuento? ¿Son importantes para la aventura? ¿Qué clase de animal incluirías?

Cuentos de Aventuras

2 ¿Cuántos protagonistas había en el cuento? ¿Quiénes eran? Si fueras el autor, ¿Cuáles personajes serían los más importantes?

Cuentos de Aventuras

3 ¿Qué cambios harías en el cuento si tuviera lugar en la antigüedad o en el futuro?

Cuentos de Aventuras

4 ¿Terminó la aventura como tú esperabas? ¿Por qué?

Cuentos de Aventuras
Question Cards

Cuentos de Aventuras

5 ¿Cuál es la aventura más memorable que has tenido tú?

Cuentos de Aventuras

6 ¿Te gustaría tener una aventura como la del cuento? ¿Por qué?

Cuentos de Aventuras

7 Describe en qué se parece o se diferencia tu aventura más memorable a la de este cuento.

Cuentos de Aventuras

8 Imagínate que eres el autor: describe otro final para el cuento.

Cuentos de Aventuras

Question Cards

Cuentos de Aventuras

9 ¿Cuál es tu momento favorito en el cuento?

Cuentos de Aventuras

10 ¿Cuál fue el evento más importante de la aventura? ¿Por qué?

Cuentos de Aventuras

11 Si hicieran una película basada en el cuento, ¿qué personaje te gustaría interpretar en la película? ¿Por qué?

Cuentos de Aventuras

12 Tú eres el autor y tienes que revisar el cuento, ¿qué cambiarías para que fuera más emocionante?

Cuentos de Aventuras
Question Cards

Cuentos de Aventuras

13 Nombra tu cuento o película de aventuras favorita. ¿Hay alguna parte de ese cuento que se pudiera incluir en éste?

Cuentos de Aventuras

14 ¿Puedes pensar en un ambiente para esta aventura que fuera más emocionante?

Cuentos de Aventuras

15 Dile al autor cuál es la mejor y peor parte de este cuento.

Cuentos de Aventuras

16 Si tuvieras que dividir este cuento en cuatro capítulos, ¿cuál sería el cuarto capítulo?

Crítica del Libro

Book Review

higher-level thinking questions

Crítica del Libro

Journal Writing Question

Write your response to the question below.
Be ready to share your response.

¿Qué parte del cuento cambiarías si fuera posible? Explica tu elección.

Crítica del Libro
Question Cards

Crítica del Libro

1 ¿Qué podría haber sucedido para que cambiara el desenlace del cuento?

Crítica del Libro

2 ¿Cómo usó el autor las imágenes para crear sensaciones en el lector?

Crítica del Libro

3 ¿Qué otro título podría tener el cuento y por qué?

Crítica del Libro

4 ¿Cuál podría ser un buen lema para hacer publicidad del libro?

Crítica del Libro
Question Cards

Crítica del Libro

5 ¿Si la acción que se desarrolla en el cuento fuera una extensión de agua, cuál sería: un río caudaloso, un arroyo sinuoso, un lago tranquilo o un mar agitado?

Crítica del Libro

6 ¿Qué símbolo escogerías para representar la personalidad del protagonista?

Crítica del Libro

7 ¿En qué otro período de tiempo podría haber tenido lugar este cuento? ¿Qué cambiará a causa del mismo?

Crítica del Libro

8 Si el comienzo del libro fuera un aperitivo, ¿qué sería?

Crítica del Libro

Question Cards

Crítica del Libro

9 Si el final del libro fuera un postre, ¿qué sería?

Crítica del Libro

10 Imagínate que te van a entrevistar como el autor del libro, ¿cuáles dirías que fueron tus razones para escribir el libro?

Crítica del Libro

11 Si fueras a escribir una crítica de este libro, ¿qué diría el encabezamiento?

Crítica del Libro

12 ¿Cuál es la moraleja de este cuento y por qué?

Crítica del Libro
Question Cards

Crítica del Libro

13 ¿Qué parte del cuento cambiarías si fuera posible? Explica tu elección.

Crítica del Libro

14 ¿Con qué personaje te identificas más y por qué?

Crítica del Libro

15 ¿Con qué personaje no estás de acuerdo en absoluto o a cuál censuras más y por qué?

Crítica del Libro

16 ¿Cuál crees que es el problema principal del cuento? ¿Te sentiste satisfecho con la solución? ¿Por qué?

Cuentos Fantásticos

Fantasy Stories

higher-level thinking questions

Cuentos Fantásticos

Journal Writing Question

Write your response to the question below.
Be ready to share your response.

¿En qué parte del cuento te sentiste más emocionado? ¿Por qué?

Cuentos Fantásticos

Question Cards

Cuentos Fantásticos

1 ¿Hay fuerzas enemigas en el relato? Si es así, ¿cuáles son?

Cuentos Fantásticos

2 ¿Qué peculiaridades o poderes tienen los personajes que no tenemos nosotros?

Cuentos Fantásticos

3 ¿Cuál es la parte que más te gusta del cuento? ¿Por qué?

Cuentos Fantásticos

4 ¿Te has sentido alguna vez como alguno de los personajes del cuento? ¿Cuándo y por qué?

Cuentos Fantásticos
Question Cards

Cuentos Fantásticos

5 Si pudieras ser uno de los personajes del cuento, ¿quién te gustaría ser y por qué?

Cuentos Fantásticos

6 ¿Qué te gustó más y qué te gustó menos en este cuento fantástico? ¿Por qué?

Cuentos Fantásticos

7 ¿Qué cuentos has leído que sean parecidos a éste?

Cuentos Fantásticos

8 Explica dos formas diferentes de solucionar el problema del cuento.

Cuentos Fantásticos
Question Cards

Cuentos Fantásticos

9 Si hubieras formado parte del cuento y tuvieras un poder especial, ¿cómo lo usarías?

Cuentos Fantásticos

10 ¿En qué se parece o se diferencia el mundo del cuento de nuestro mundo? ¿Por qué?

Cuentos Fantásticos

11 ¿En qué parte del cuento te sentiste más emocionado? ¿Por qué?

Cuentos Fantásticos

12 ¿Cuál es la parte menos creíble del cuento? ¿Cómo puedes lograr que sea más creíble?

Cuentos Fantásticos
Question Cards

Cuentos Fantásticos

13 ¿Cuál es el problema más importante al que se enfrenta el protagonista?

Cuentos Fantásticos

14 ¿Cómo ha logrado el autor que el cuento sea creíble?

Cuentos Fantásticos

15 Si fueras dibujante, ¿cómo ilustrarías este libro?

Cuentos Fantásticos

16 Describe cómo te imaginas al autor.

Cuentos de Misterio

Mystery Stories

higher-level thinking questions

Cuentos de Misterio

Journal Writing Question

Write your response to the question below.
Be ready to share your response.

¿Qué pistas dio el autor para ayudarte a resolver el misterio?

Cuentos de Misterio

Question Cards

Cuentos de Misterio

¿Qué personaje del libro se parece más a ti? ¿Por qué?

Cuentos de Misterio

¿Qué pistas dio el autor para ayudarte a resolver el misterio?

Cuentos de Misterio

¿Qué parte del libro te gustó más?

Cuentos de Misterio

¿Te gustó el final? ¿Por qué?

Cuentos de Misterio

Question Cards

Cuentos de Misterio

5 ¿Crees que las cosas que ocurren en el libro pueden suceder en la vida real? ¿Por qué?

Cuentos de Misterio

6 ¿Cómo consiguió el autor crear más suspenso?

Cuentos de Misterio

7 Nombra el programa de televisión o la película que se parezcan más a este cuento. ¿Por qué?

Cuentos de Misterio

8 Imagínate que eres el autor: ¿cómo crearías más suspenso?

Cuentos de Misterio
Question Cards

Cuentos de Misterio

9 Si escribieras un cuento de misterio, ¿en qué ambiente se desarrollaría?

Cuentos de Misterio

10 ¿Resolviste tú el misterio antes de que se resolviera en el libro? En caso afirmativo, ¿cómo lo lograste?

Cuentos de Misterio

11 ¿Hay algunos personajes que eliminarías o cambiarías?

Cuentos de Misterio

12 ¿Cuándo cambiaste de parecer sobre lo que iba a suceder?

Cuentos de Misterio
Question Cards

Cuentos de Misterio

13 ¿Era el ambiente en que se desenvolvía el cuento crucial para el misterio?

Cuentos de Misterio

14 ¿Logró despistarte el autor? Si es así, ¿cómo? Si no lo logró, ¿por qué no?

Cuentos de Misterio

15 Diles a tus compañeros de equipo cosas sobre el personaje que el autor se olvidó de decirnos.

Cuentos de Misterio

16 Si este cuento tuviera lugar en el año 2050, ¿qué cambios tendrías que hacer?

Posibilidades Poéticas

Poetry Possibilities

higher-level thinking questions

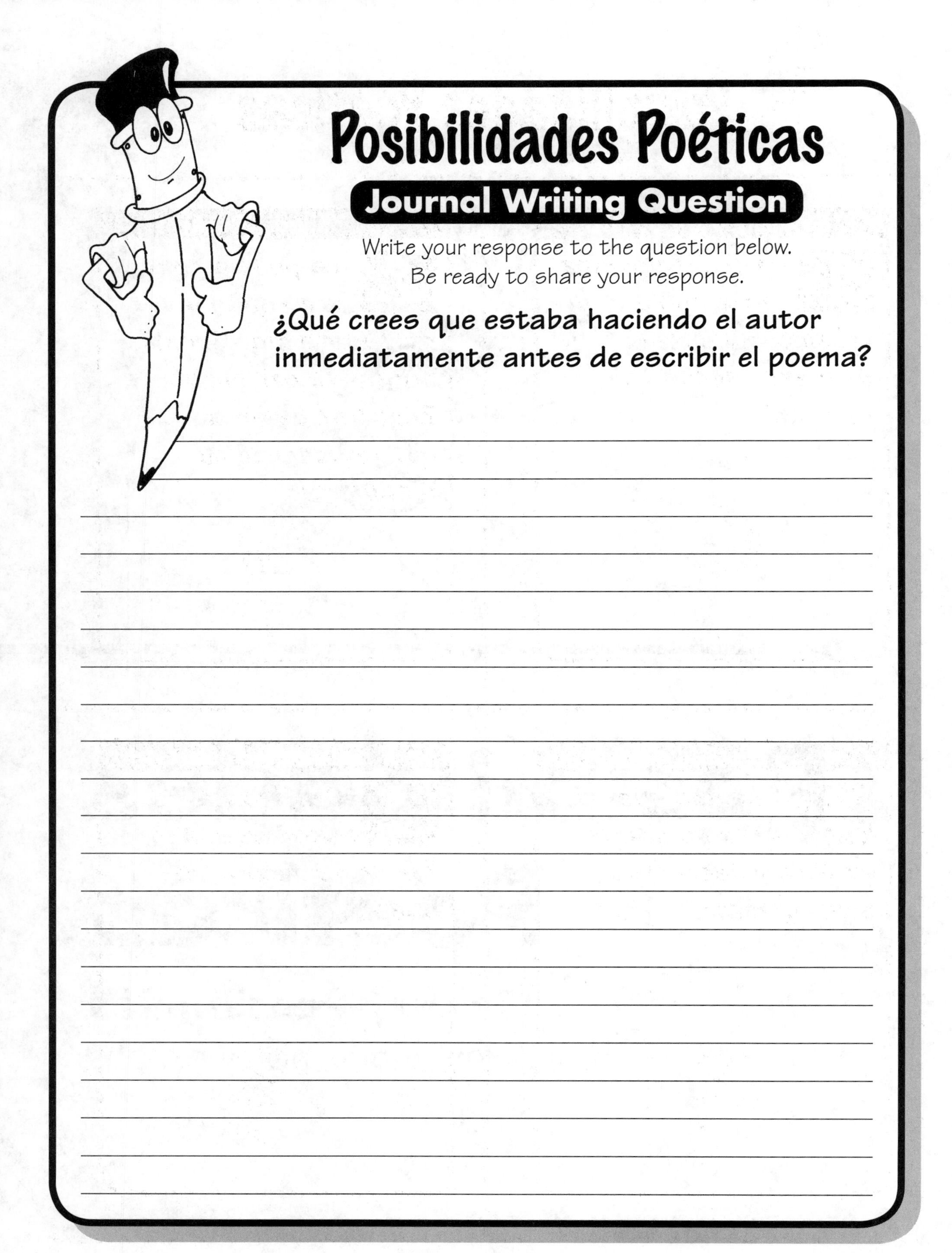

Posibilidades Poéticas

Journal Writing Question

Write your response to the question below.
Be ready to share your response.

¿Qué crees que estaba haciendo el autor inmediatamente antes de escribir el poema?

Posibilidades Poéticas
Question Cards

Posibilidades Poéticas

1 Si a este poema se le pusiera música, ¿qué clase de instrumentos se usarían?

Posibilidades Poéticas

2 La poesía crea a menudo una respuesta emocional por parte del lector. Elige una palabra que represente tu respuesta.

Posibilidades Poéticas

3 Imagina que este poema es un libro y describe al protagonista.

Posibilidades Poéticas

4 Sugiérele al autor alguna forma de mejorar su poema.

Posibilidades Poéticas
Question Cards

Posibilidades Poéticas

5 ¿Puedes mencionar otro título posible para el poema?

Posibilidades Poéticas

6 ¿Por qué crees que el autor quiso que el poema rimara, o no rimara?

Posibilidades Poéticas

7 ¿Qué crees que estaba haciendo el autor inmediatamente antes de escribir el poema?

Posibilidades Poéticas

8 ¿A quién crees que estaba escribiendo el autor y por qué?

Posibilidades Poéticas

Question Cards

Posibilidades Poéticas

9 Si el poema sirviera de inspiración para un programa de televisión, ¿qué clase de programa sería: cómico, de acción y aventuras o dramático? ¿Por qué?

Posibilidades Poéticas

10 Si el poema fuera una flor, ¿sería una rosa con espinas, un tulipán delicado, una amapola silvestre o __________?

Posibilidades Poéticas

11 Elige una palabra que describa el ritmo del poema.

Posibilidades Poéticas

12 ¿Cómo crees que se sentía el autor mientras escribía el poema?

Posibilidades Poéticas

Question Cards

Posibilidades Poéticas

13 ¿Qué crees que quiso decir el autor cuando escribió el poema?

Posibilidades Poéticas

14 Imagínate que el poema estuviera escrito en la parte interior de una tarjeta de felicitación. Describe el dibujo que habría en la portada de la tarjeta.

Posibilidades Poéticas

15 ¿Qué hubiera sentido un lector al leer el poema hace unos 100 años? ¿Por qué?

Posibilidades Poéticas

16 ¿Tendrá algún sentido el poema dentro de 100 años? Explica tu respuesta.

Preguntas Previas: Misterios

Prewriting: Mysteries

higher-level thinking questions

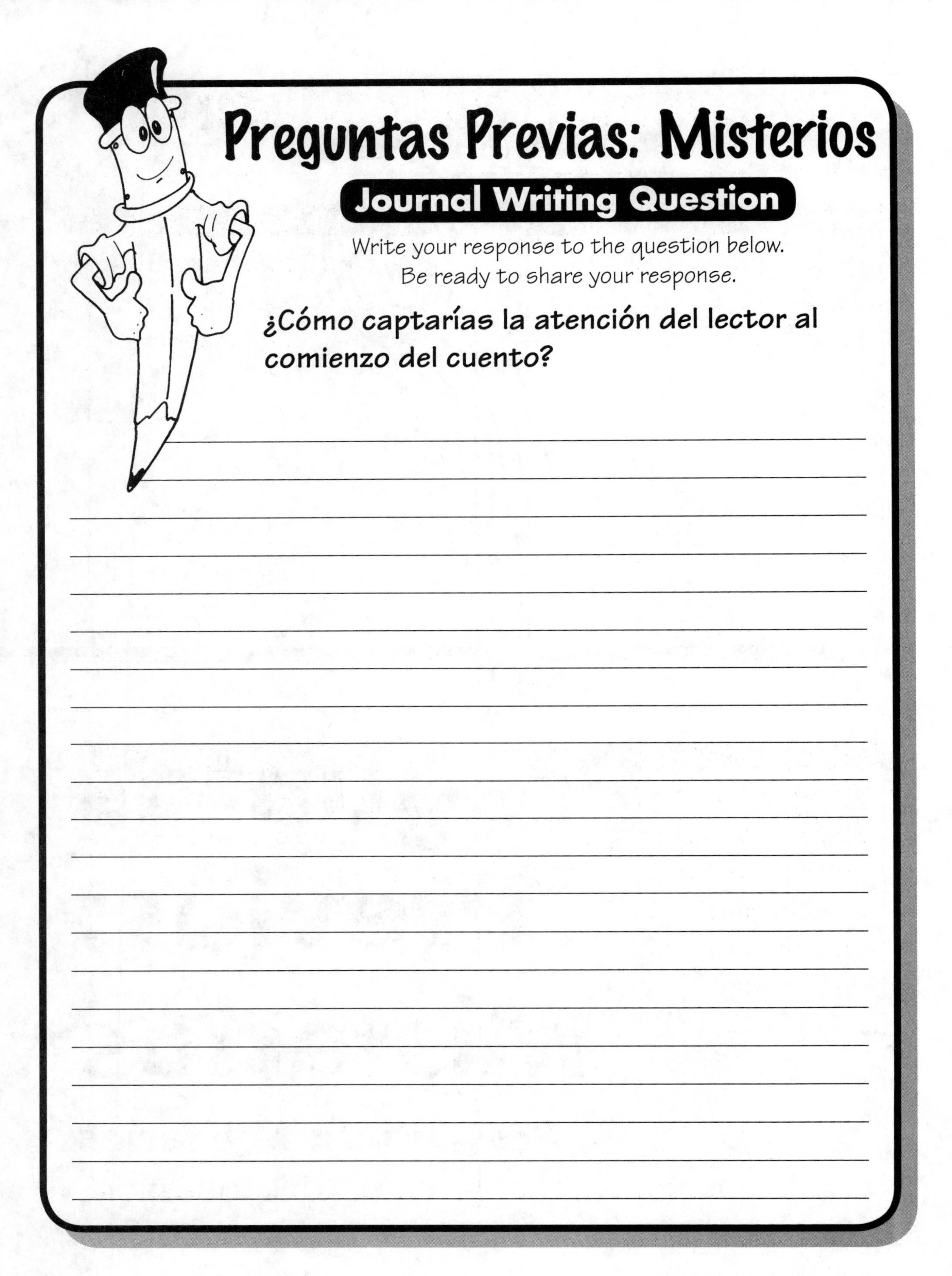

Preguntas Previas: Misterios

Journal Writing Question

Write your response to the question below.
Be ready to share your response.

¿Cómo captarías la atención del lector al comienzo del cuento?

Preguntas Previas: Misterios

Question Cards

Preguntas Previas: Misterios

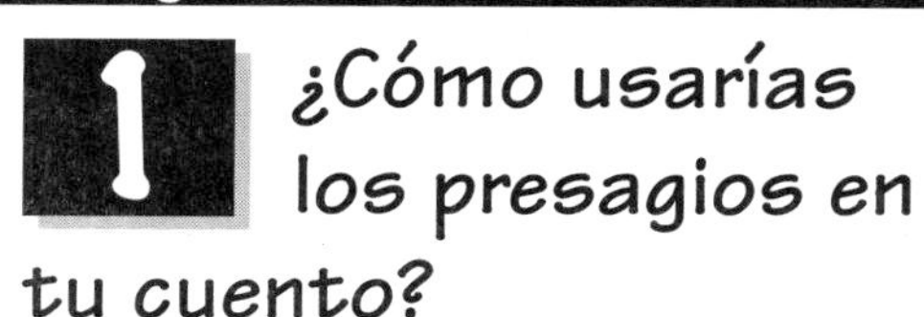

1 ¿Cómo usarías los presagios en tu cuento?

Preguntas Previas: Misterios

2 ¿Cómo captarías la atención del lector al comienzo del cuento?

Preguntas Previas: Misterios

3 ¿Qué características podría tener el protagonista que proporcionaran un mayor misterio al cuento?

Preguntas Previas: Misterios

4 ¿Cómo darías más suspenso al cuento?

Preguntas Previas: Misterios

Question Cards

Preguntas Previas: Misterios

5 ¿Sabrá el lector más cosas sobre el misterio que los personajes? Explica tu elección.

Preguntas Previas: Misterios

6 ¿Cómo se resolverá el misterio?

Preguntas Previas: Misterios

7 ¿Cómo aumentará el misterio el ambiente en el que se desarrolla el cuento?

Preguntas Previas: Misterios

8 ¿Cómo te gustaría que se sintiera el lector al final del cuento?

Preguntas Previas: Misterios

Question Cards

Preguntas Previas: Misterios

9 Explica por qué has decidido incluir/excluir un héroe o una heroína.

Preguntas Previas: Misterios

10 ¿Qué palabras puedes usar para describir la acción del cuento?

Preguntas Previas: Misterios

11 ¿Qué pistas puedes dar al lector para revelar la trama misteriosa?

Preguntas Previas: Misterios

12 ¿Puedes mencionar un posible título para tu cuento?

Preguntas Previas: Misterios
Question Cards

Preguntas Previas: Misterios

13 ¿Podría haber algún crimen en el cuento? ¿Por qué?

Preguntas Previas: Misterios

14 ¿Qué evento será el punto culminante del cuento?

Preguntas Previas: Misterios

15 ¿Qué eventos conducen al punto culminante del cuento?

Preguntas Previas: Misterios

16 ¿Narrará el cuento uno de los personajes o habrá un observador/narrador?

Preguntas Previas: Biografía/ Autobiografía

Prewriting: Biography/Autobiography

higher-level thinking questions

Preguntas Previas: Biografía/Autobiografía

Journal Writing Question

Write your response to the question below.
Be ready to share your response.

¿Cuáles consideras que son los puntos fuertes y débiles de tu sujeto? ¿Por qué?

Preguntas Previas: Biografía/Autobiografía

Question Cards

Preguntas Previas: Biografía/Autobiografía

1 ¿Cómo podrías organizar la información para mostrar el desarrollo emocional, intelectual y físico del sujeto?

Preguntas Previas: Biografía/Autobiografía

2 ¿Cómo podrías describir mejor el evento más importante de la vida de tu sujeto?

Preguntas Previas: Biografía/Autobiografía

3 ¿Qué palabras podrías usar para describir la personalidad de tu sujeto?

Preguntas Previas: Biografía/Autobiografía

4 Completa la siguiente frase. El sujeto es como ________ porque ____________.

Preguntas Previas: Biografía/Autobiografía

Question Cards

Preguntas Previas: Biografía/Autobiografía

5 ¿Cuál consideras que es el mayor logro de tu sujeto? Explica tu elección.

Preguntas Previas: Biografía/Autobiografía

6 ¿Cuáles consideras que son los puntos fuertes y débiles de tu sujeto? ¿Por qué?

Preguntas Previas: Biografía/Autobiografía

7 Elige un símbolo que represente a tu sujeto. Explica tu elección.

Preguntas Previas: Biografía/Autobiografía

8 ¿Quién crees que tuvo mayor influencia en tu sujeto? ¿Por qué?

Preguntas Previas: Biografía/Autobiografía

Question Cards

Preguntas Previas: Biografía/Autobiografía

9 ¿Por qué es importante la descripción física de tu sujeto en la historia de su vida?

Preguntas Previas: Biografía/Autobiografía

10 ¿Qué sería diferente si tu sujeto no hubiera existido?

Preguntas Previas: Biografía/Autobiografía

11 ¿Cuál crees que fue el mayor reto al que se enfrentó el sujeto?

Preguntas Previas: Biografía/Autobiografía

12 La cultura juega un papel muy importante en quiénes somos. ¿Qué papel tienen los antecedentes culturales en la vida del sujeto?

Preguntas Previas: Biografía/Autobiografía

Question Cards

Preguntas Previas: Biografía/Autobiografía

13 ¿Por cuál acción será más recordado el sujeto?

Preguntas Previas: Biografía/Autobiografía

14 ¿Qué te dicen las acciones del sujeto sobre sus principios y valores morales?

Preguntas Previas: Biografía/Autobiografía

15 Si el sujeto hubiera vivido en otro país, ¿qué hubiera sido diferente?

Preguntas Previas: Biografía/Autobiografía

16 ¿Cuál sería el mejor lema para divulgar la historia de su vida?

Preguntas Previas: Cuentos

Prewriting: Stories

higher-level thinking questions

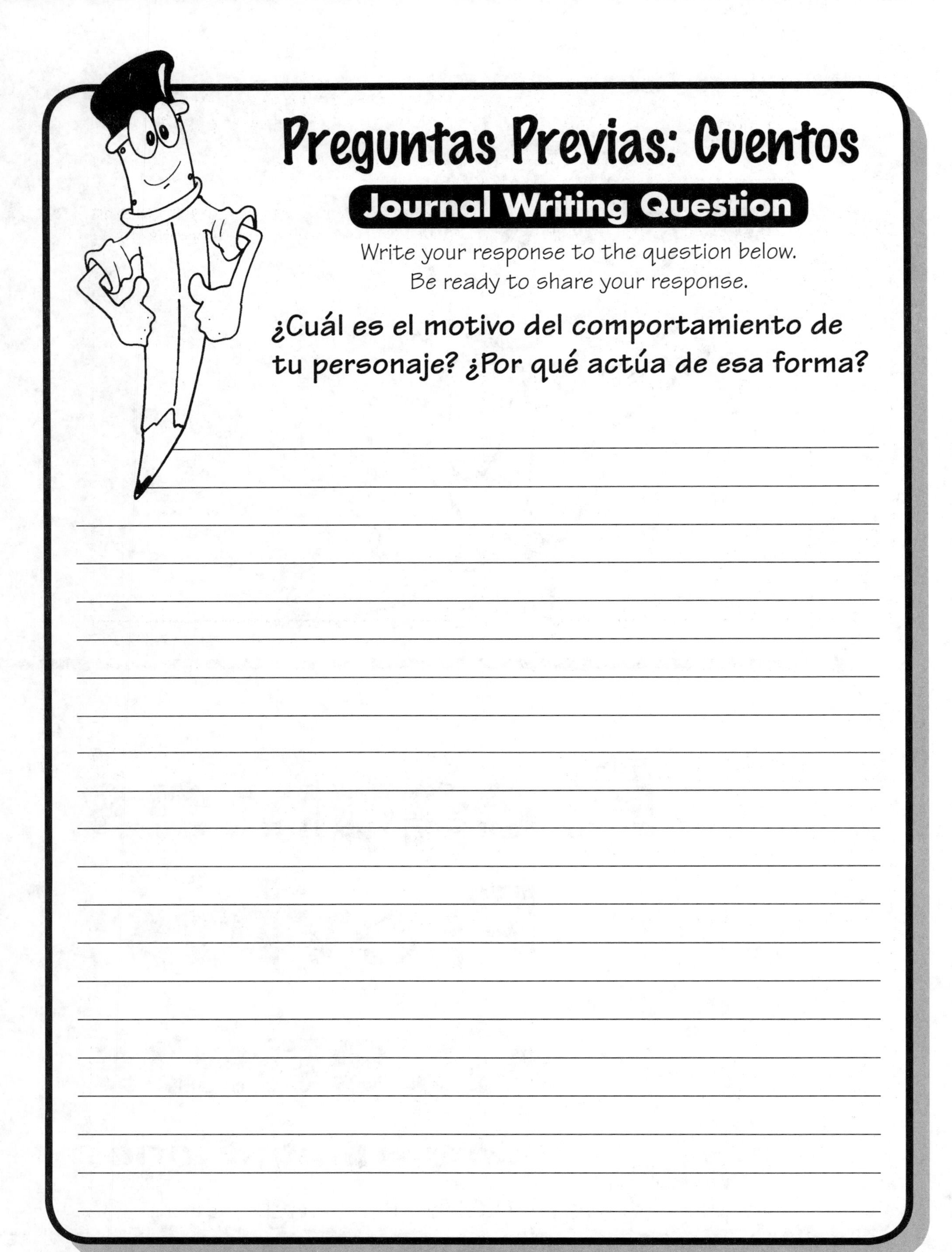

Preguntas Previas: Cuentos

Journal Writing Question

Write your response to the question below.
Be ready to share your response.

¿Cuál es el motivo del comportamiento de tu personaje? ¿Por qué actúa de esa forma?

Preguntas Previas: Cuentos
Question Cards

Preguntas Previas: Cuentos

1 ¿Cómo le explicarías al lector la personalidad del protagonista?

Preguntas Previas: Cuentos

2 ¿En qué área tendría lugar tu cuento? ¿Qué pistas puedes usar para dar a conocer al lector el ambiente en que se desarrolla?

Preguntas Previas: Cuentos

3 ¿Cómo podrías captar mejor la atención del lector al comienzo del cuento?

Preguntas Previas: Cuentos

4 ¿Cómo se desarrollará la trama? ¿Qué sucederá primero, después ...?

Preguntas Previas: Cuentos
Question Cards

Preguntas Previas: Cuentos

5 La relación entre los personajes es muy importante en un cuento. ¿Con quién tendrá el protagonista la relación más importante?

Preguntas Previas: Cuentos

6 ¿Cómo puede jugar el tiempo un papel importante en tu cuento?

Preguntas Previas: Cuentos

7 ¿Qué pistas podrías usar para dar a conocer al lector cómo podría terminar el cuento?

Preguntas Previas: Cuentos

8 ¿Cuál será el problema o conflicto principal en tu cuento?

Preguntas Previas: Cuentos
Question Cards

Preguntas Previas: Cuentos

9 ¿Cuáles son las dos soluciones posibles del problema principal del cuento?

Preguntas Previas: Cuentos

10 ¿Qué personaje puede contar mejor el cuento y por qué?

Preguntas Previas: Cuentos

11 ¿Cuándo alcanzará su punto culminante la acción del cuento? Explica tu razonamiento.

Preguntas Previas: Cuentos

12 ¿Cuál es el motivo del comportamiento de tu personaje? ¿Por qué actúa de esa forma?

Preguntas Previas: Cuentos
Question Cards

Preguntas Previas: Cuentos

13 ¿Cuál podría ser la moraleja de tu cuento?

Preguntas Previas: Cuentos

14 ¿Cómo esperas que se sienta el lector al leer el final?

Preguntas Previas: Cuentos

15 ¿Cómo podrías llamar tu cuento?

Preguntas Previas: Cuentos

16 ¿Cómo podrías ilustrar tu cuento?

Personajes del Cuento

Story Characters

higher-level thinking questions

Personajes del Cuento

Journal Writing Question

Write your response to the question below.
Be ready to share your response.

¿Qué le sucederá al personaje en la continuación del libro?

Personajes del Cuento

Question Cards

Personajes del Cuento

1 ¿Qué hizo el protagonista para que te caiga bien o mal?

Personajes del Cuento

2 ¿De qué forma es importante para el cuento el papel que desempeñan los personajes secundarios?

Personajes del Cuento

3 ¿Qué sucedería si el protagonista fuera de diferente sexo o de una especie diferente?

Personajes del Cuento

4 ¿Quién podría sustituir al protagonista? Elige un personaje de un programa de caricaturas.

Personajes del Cuento
Question Cards

Personajes del Cuento

5 ¿Qué color describe al protagonista? ¿Por qué?

Personajes del Cuento

6 ¿Cómo evolucionó el personaje desde el comienzo hasta el final?

Personajes del Cuento

7 ¿Qué podría haber hecho el personaje al comienzo para cambiar el desenlace del cuento?

Personajes del Cuento

8 ¿Cómo describirías el personaje a una persona ciega?

Personajes del Cuento
Question Cards

Personajes del Cuento

9 ¿Qué puedes decir acerca de la vida familiar del protagonista?

Personajes del Cuento

10 ¿En qué se parece el protagonista a ti? ¿En qué se diferencia?

Personajes del Cuento

11 ¿Qué le sucederá al personaje en la continuación del libro?

Personajes del Cuento

12 ¿Por qué te gustaría ser amigo del personaje? Si no te gustaría, ¿por qué no?

Personajes del Cuento
Question Cards

Personajes del Cuento

13 ¿Cuándo te enfrentaste a un problema en tu vida que fuese parecido al problema con que se enfrentó el personaje?

Personajes del Cuento

14 ¿A quién acudió el personaje en busca de apoyo y comprensión? ¿A quién podría acudir el personaje?

Personajes del Cuento

15 ¿Dónde estará el personaje dentro de 20 años?

Personajes del Cuento

16 ¿De qué forma sería diferente el personaje si el cuento fuera real o ficticio?

La Trama del Cuento

Story Plot

higher-level thinking questions

La Trama del Cuento

Journal Writing Question

Write your response to the question below.
Be ready to share your response.

¿Cuál es el problema principal que se presenta en el cuento?

La Trama del Cuento

Question Cards

La Trama del Cuento

1 ¿Cómo capta el autor la atención del lector al comienzo del cuento?

La Trama del Cuento

2 ¿En qué parte del cuento alcanza su punto culminante la acción?

La Trama del Cuento

3 ¿Cómo influye el ambiente en la acción del cuento?

La Trama del Cuento

4 ¿Cuál es el problema principal que se presenta en el cuento?

La Trama del Cuento

Question Cards

La Trama del Cuento

5 ¿Qué parte del argumento te gustó más? Explica tus razones.

La Trama del Cuento

6 ¿Qué influencia tiene la edad del protagonista en sus acciones?

La Trama del Cuento

7 ¿Cómo afectaría el cambio de uno de los eventos importantes al desenlace del cuento?

La Trama del Cuento

8 ¿A qué te recuerda la acción del cuento: un viaje en la montaña rusa, una caminata sin prisas, un viaje en balsa por aguas turbulentas o ____________?
¿Por qué?

La Trama del Cuento
Question Cards

La Trama del Cuento

9 ¿Qué palabra usarías para describir el argumento? ¿Por qué?

La Trama del Cuento

10 ¿Por qué el autor finalizó el cuento de esa forma?

La Trama del Cuento

11 Escribe otro final para el cuento sin cambiar el argumento.

La Trama del Cuento

12 ¿En qué parte del cuento sentiste una emoción más intensa? ¿Por qué te hizo sentir emoción esa parte?

La Trama del Cuento
Question Cards

La Trama del Cuento

13 ¿Cuál sería la continuación del cuento?

La Trama del Cuento

14 ¿Qué eventos del cuento te podrían haber sucedido a ti?

La Trama del Cuento

15 ¿Qué evento tuvo el mayor impacto en el desenlace? ¿Por qué?

La Trama del Cuento

16 ¿A qué otro cuento te recuerda éste?

Ambiente del Cuento

Story Setting

higher-level thinking questions

Ambiente del Cuento

Journal Writing Question

Write your response to the question below.
Be ready to share your response.

¿En qué forma depende la acción del cuento del ambiente?

Ambiente del Cuento
Question Cards

Ambiente del Cuento

1 ¿Qué pistas usó el autor en el ambiente para explicar el cuento?

Ambiente del Cuento

2 ¿Cómo afectó el clima a la acción del cuento?

Ambiente del Cuento

3 ¿Qué influencia tuvieron los valores sociales de la época en los personajes?

Ambiente del Cuento

4 ¿En qué otra época pudo haber tenido lugar el cuento?

Ambiente del Cuento
Question Cards

Ambiente del Cuento

5 ¿En qué otro sitio pudo haber tenido lugar el cuento sin afectar la trama?

Ambiente del Cuento

6 ¿Cómo se podría representar el ambiente con un solo color?

Ambiente del Cuento

7 ¿En qué forma podría haber afectado la tecnología moderna a la acción o al desenlace del cuento?

Ambiente del Cuento

8 ¿Cómo un cambio de los medios de transporte podría haber afectado al desenlace?

Ambiente del Cuento

Question Cards

Ambiente del Cuento

9 ¿Qué material escogerías para describir el ambiente del cuento: pintura, arcilla o acuarelas? Explica tu elección.

Ambiente del Cuento

10 ¿De qué forma depende la acción del cuento del ambiente?

Ambiente del Cuento

11 ¿Cómo describiría un agente de viajes el ambiente del cuento?

Ambiente del Cuento

12 ¿En dónde tuvo lugar el cuento?

Ambiente del Cuento
Question Cards

Ambiente del Cuento

13 ¿Cuándo tuvo lugar el cuento?

Ambiente del Cuento

14 Nombra el continente en que tuvo lugar el cuento. ¿Qué cambios se podrían haber producido en el cuento si hubiera tenido lugar en otro continente?

Ambiente del Cuento

15 Si el ambiente del cuento se presentara en una fotografía de una revista, ¿qué diría el pie de fotografía?

Ambiente del Cuento

16 ¿Te gustaría vivir en la época en que tiene lugar el cuento? ¿Por qué?

Estructura del Cuento

Story Structure

higher-level thinking questions

Estructura del Cuento

Journal Writing Question

Write your response to the question below.
Be ready to share your response.

Escribe un nuevo final que te guste más para el cuento.

Estructura del Cuento
Question Cards

Estructura del Cuento

1 ¿Cuál era el conflicto principal del cuento?

Estructura del Cuento

2 ¿Cómo nos hizo sentir el autor que el conflicto era importante?

Estructura del Cuento

3 Si tuvieras que volver a escribir el cuento para un período de tiempo diferente, ¿en qué época tendría lugar? ¿Cómo cambiaría el cuento?

Estructura del Cuento

4 Si tuvieras que situar el cuento un lugar diferente, ¿en dónde se desarrollaría? ¿Por qué? ¿Cómo cambiaría el cuento?

Estructura del Cuento
Question Cards

Estructura del Cuento

5 ¿Hubo algún momento en que el autor te hizo sentir más en suspenso?

Estructura del Cuento

6 Hay conflictos que son personales, como cuando quieres algo o desearías que algo no fuera así. ¿Qué clase de conflictos tenía el personaje?

Estructura del Cuento

7 Trata de mejorar el cuento poniendo o quitando un personaje. ¿Quién sería? ¿Cómo mejoraría el cuento?

Estructura del Cuento

8 ¿Cuánto tiempo transcurrió desde el comienzo hasta el final del cuento? ¿Cómo crees que sería mejor el cuento: si durara más o menos? ¿Por qué?

Estructura del Cuento

Question Cards

Estructura del Cuento

9 Escribe un nuevo final que te guste más para el cuento.

Estructura del Cuento

10 ¿Cuál fue la causa de que el cuento terminara como lo hizo: la suerte, el trabajo duro, la habilidad o una idea brillante del personaje?

Estructura del Cuento

11 ¿En qué momento te gustó más el protagonista? ¿Y menos?

Estructura del Cuento

12 Viste al protagonista con ropa diferente. ¿Por qué escogiste un traje así?

Estructura del Cuento
Question Cards

Estructura del Cuento

13 ¿Te sorprendió el final? ¿Por qué?

Estructura del Cuento

14 ¿Qué pistas nos dio el autor acerca de cómo terminaría el cuento?

Estructura del Cuento

15 Ponle un nuevo nombre a uno de los personajes del cuento que vaya mejor con su personalidad. Explica por qué.

Estructura del Cuento

16 Si el protagonista encontrara a alguien herido en la calle, ¿le prestaría ayuda? ¿Por qué crees que sí?

Vocabulario

Vocabulary

higher-level thinking questions

Vocabulario

Journal Writing Question

Write your response to the question below.
Be ready to share your response.

Parafrasea la definición de la palabra del vocabulario que viene en el diccionario.

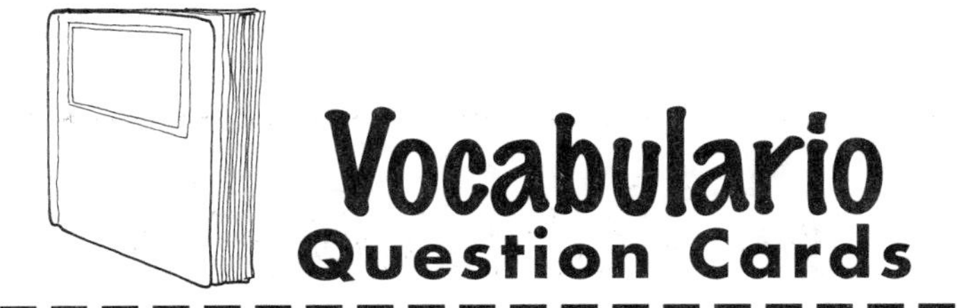

Vocabulario
Question Cards

Vocabulario

1 Si la palabra del vocabulario formara parte de una respuesta, ¿cuál sería la pregunta?

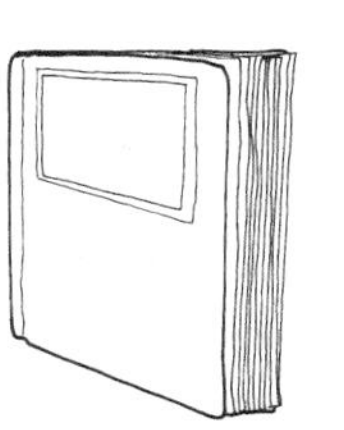

Vocabulario

2 ¿Cómo puedes representar el significado de las palabras con un símbolo?

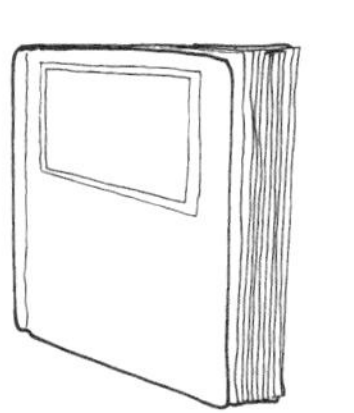

Vocabulario

3 Parafrasea la definición de la palabra del vocabulario que viene en el diccionario.

Vocabulario

4 Usa la palabra del vocabulario en una oración exclamativa.

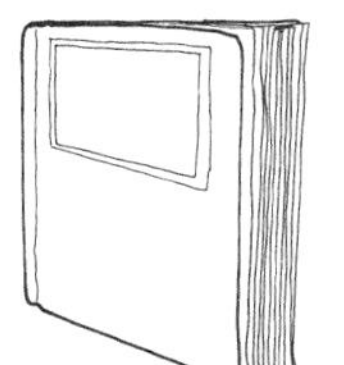

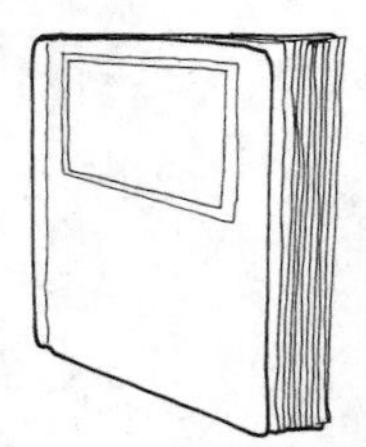

Vocabulario
Question Cards

Vocabulario

5 Menciona una posible pista de la palabra del vocabulario para un crucigrama.

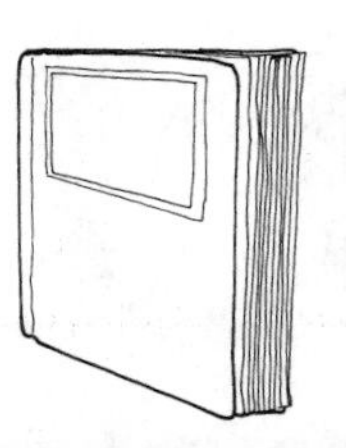

Vocabulario

6 Usa la palabra del vocabulario en una figura de dicción (metáfora o símil).

Vocabulario

7 Añade un prefijo y un sufijo a la palabra del vocabulario y di cuál es el significado de la nueva palabra.

Vocabulario

8 Nombra dos sinónimos de la palabra del vocabulario.

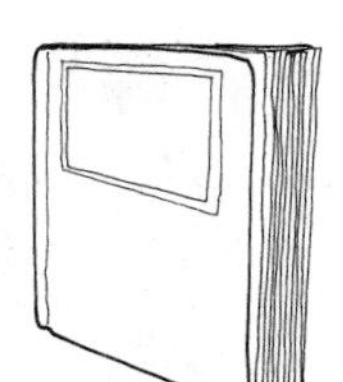

Vocabulario
Question Cards

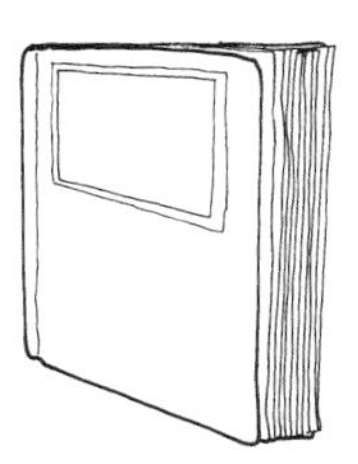

Vocabulario

9 Da dos antónimos de la palabra del vocabulario.

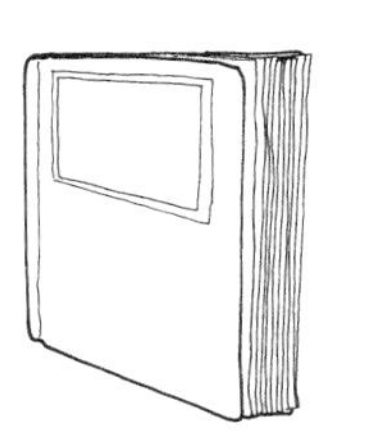

Vocabulario

10 ¿Qué otras palabras puedes crear con las letras de la palabra del vocabulario?

Vocabulario

11 ¿Cuáles son las palabras guía del diccionario para la palabra del vocabulario?

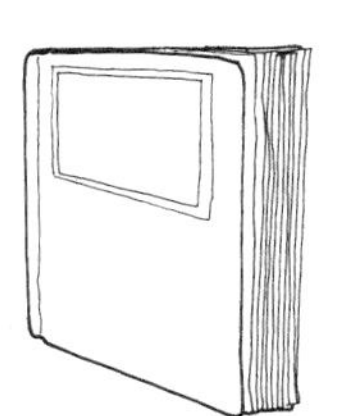

Vocabulario

12 ¿Qué número de sílabas dan en el diccionario?

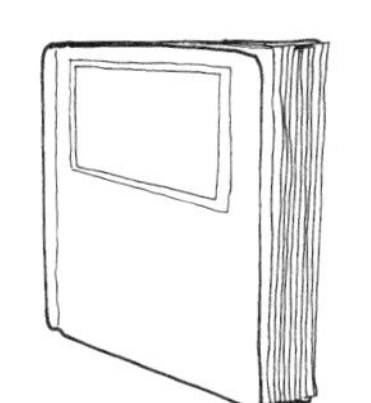

Vocabulario
Question Cards

Vocabulario

13 Compara las diferentes definiciones de la palabra del vocabulario y establece contrastes entre las mismas.

Vocabulario

14 Usa la palabra del vocabulario en una oración con aliteración.

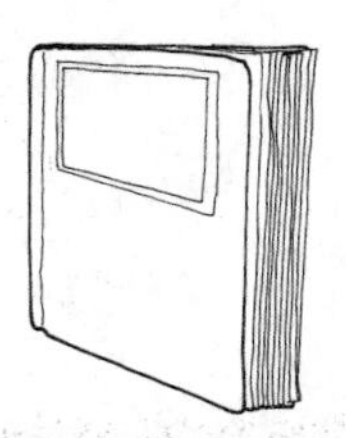

Vocabulario

15 Nombra dos palabras que rimen con la palabra del vocabulario.

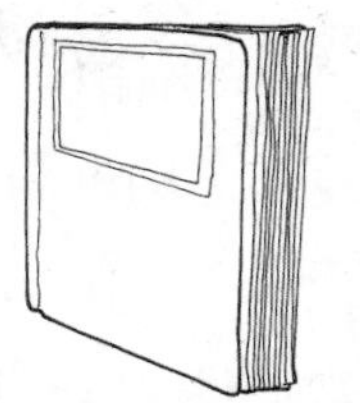

Vocabulario

16 ¿Qué parte del lenguaje es la palabra del vocabulario? ¿En qué forma podría usarse como otra parte del lenguaje?

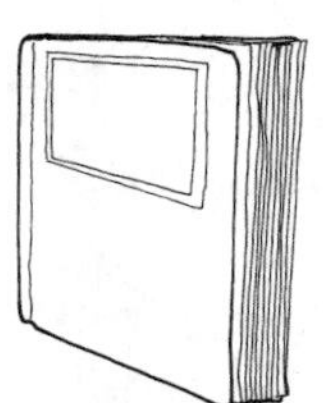

Eventos de Actualidad

Current Events

higher-level thinking questions

Eventos de Actualidad

Journal Writing Question

Write your response to the question below.
Be ready to share your response.

¿Cómo se representaría mejor este evento o asunto en la televisión: en forma de película, de serie, de un anuncio o como el tema de un programa de entrevistas?

Eventos de Actualidad

Question Cards

Eventos de Actualidad

1 Vas a escribirle una carta al director del diario sobre este tema. ¿Qué dirías y por qué?

Eventos de Actualidad

2 ¿De qué forma sería diferente este evento/asunto si hubiera ocurrido hace 100 años?

Eventos de Actualidad

3 ¿Quién se ha visto más afectado por este evento o asunto: algunos ciudadanos, un estado determinado, un país o el mundo? Explica tu respuesta.

Eventos de Actualidad

4 Tienes la oportunidad de entrevistar a los personajes implicados en el evento. ¿Qué les preguntarías?

Eventos de Actualidad
Question Cards

Eventos de Actualidad

5 La mayoría de las acciones están sujetas a la relación causa y efecto. ¿Consideras que este evento o asunto es la "causa" o el "efecto"? Explica tu opinión.

Eventos de Actualidad

6 ¿Cómo se muestran en este evento o asunto los principios morales y los valores de hoy?

Eventos de Actualidad

7 ¿Te hubiera gustado formar parte de este evento o asunto? ¿Por qué?

Eventos de Actualidad

8 ¿Cómo se representaría mejor este evento o asunto en la televisión: en forma de película, de serie, de un anuncio o como el tema de un programa de entrevistas?

Eventos de Actualidad
Question Cards

Eventos de Actualidad

9 ¿Qué papel desempeñó la tecnología moderna en este evento o asunto? ¿Cómo cambiaría con la tecnología o sin ella?

Eventos de Actualidad

10 ¿Sobre qué trataría una historia complementaria?

Eventos de Actualidad

11 ¿Qué otros asuntos o temas de actualidad están relacionados con este tema? Explica la relación existente.

Eventos de Actualidad

12 Completa la siguiente analogía: Este evento o asunto es como un ________ porque ________________.

Eventos de Actualidad
Question Cards

Eventos de Actualidad

13 Nombra las personas más importantes implicadas en este evento o asunto. ¿Qué diferencia habría sin ellas?

Eventos de Actualidad

14 Dicen que la historia se repite. ¿Qué evento o asunto histórico es similar a éste?

Eventos de Actualidad

15 ¿Qué partes de este evento o asunto están bajo el control humano? ¿Qué partes controla la naturaleza?

Eventos de Actualidad

16 ¿Podría ocurrir este evento o asunto en otro país que tuviera un gobierno diferente? ¿Por qué?

Geografía Cultural

Geography: Cultural

higher-level thinking questions

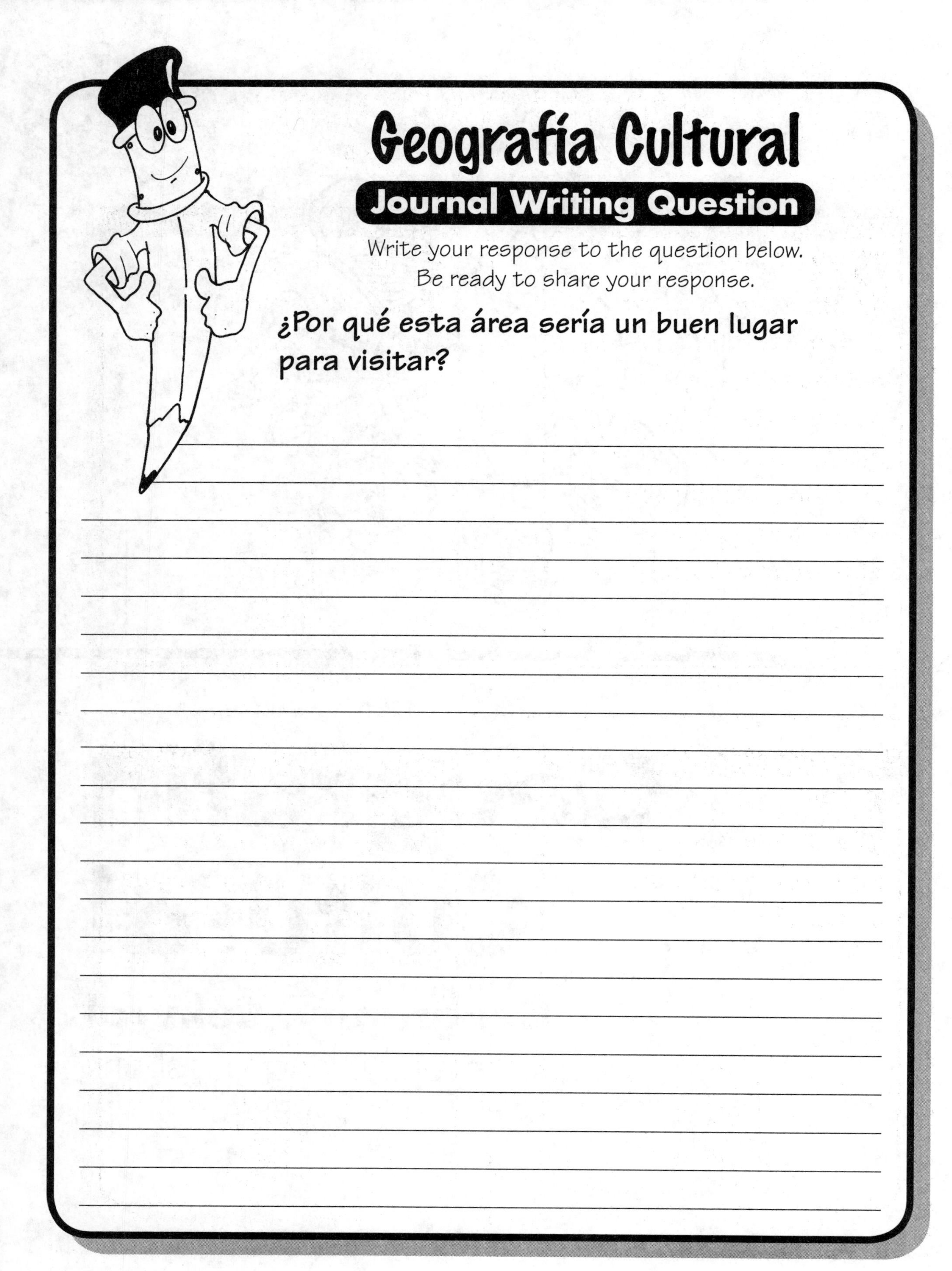

Geografía Cultural

Journal Writing Question

Write your response to the question below.
Be ready to share your response.

¿Por qué esta área sería un buen lugar para visitar?

Geografía Cultural
Question Cards

Geografía Cultural

1 Tanto la geografía como el clima influyen en las actividades de una cultura. Considerando ambos puntos, ¿qué tipo de actividades recreativas podría disfrutar esta cultura?

Geografía Cultural

2 ¿Por qué esta área sería un buen lugar para visitar?

Geografía Cultural

3 ¿Por qué se interesaría un historiador en esta cultura?

Geografía Cultural

4 Imagínate a ti mismo en una excavación arqueológica del área. ¿Qué te diría acerca de esta cultura?

Geografía Cultural
Question Cards

Geografía Cultural

5 ¿Qué aspecto podrían tener las obras de arte de esta cultura?

Geografía Cultural

6 ¿Qué valores podrían ser importantes para esta cultura?

Geografía Cultural

7 ¿Qué clase de refugio es el apropiado para esta área? ¿Cómo han cambiado las casas del área a lo largo de los siglos?

Geografía Cultural

8 ¿Qué podemos aprender acerca de esta antigua cultura a través de los juguetes de sus niños?

Geografía Cultural
Question Cards

Geografía Cultural

9 ¿Qué tiene en común tu cultura con esta cultura?

Geografía Cultural

10 Los idiomas cambian constantemente. ¿Por qué el idioma de esta cultura ha podido cambiar a lo largo de los siglos?

Geografía Cultural

11 ¿Podría considerarse a esta zona como un crisol cultural? ¿Por qué?

Geografía Cultural

12 ¿Cómo influye la cercanía a un río en la cultura del área?

Geografía Cultural
Question Cards

Geografía Cultural

13 ¿Por qué los prejuicios culturales podrían ser un problema en esta área?

Geografía Cultural

14 ¿Por qué alguien elegiría vivir en esta área?

Geografía Cultural

15 ¿De qué forma sería diferente esta cultura si no tuviera fronteras?

Geografía Cultural

16 ¿A qué problemas se enfrentará esta cultura dentro de 100 años?

Geografía Económica

Geography: Economical

higher-level thinking questions

Geografía Económica

Journal Writing Question

Write your response to the question below.
Be ready to share your response.

¿Cómo podría cambiar la economía del área en los próximos 100 años?

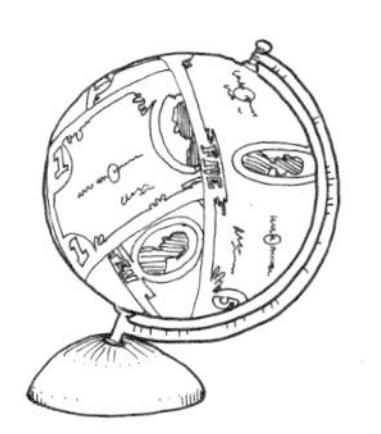

Geografía Económica
Question Cards

Geografía Económica

1 ¿De qué otra forma se pueden usar los recursos naturales del área?

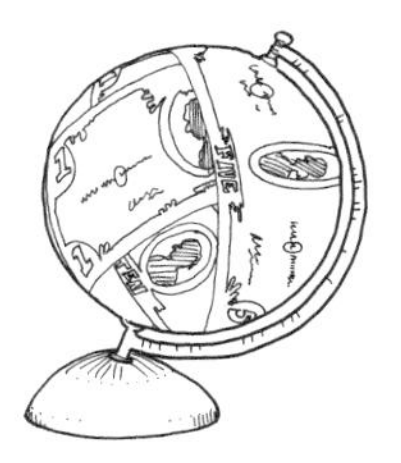

Geografía Económica

2 ¿Qué necesitarían importar los habitantes del área?

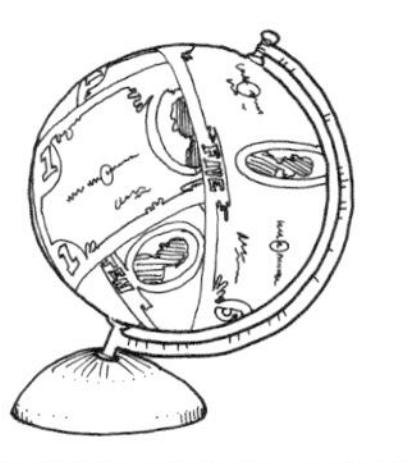

Geografía Económica

3 ¿Se puede considerar el clima del área como un recurso natural? ¿Por qué?

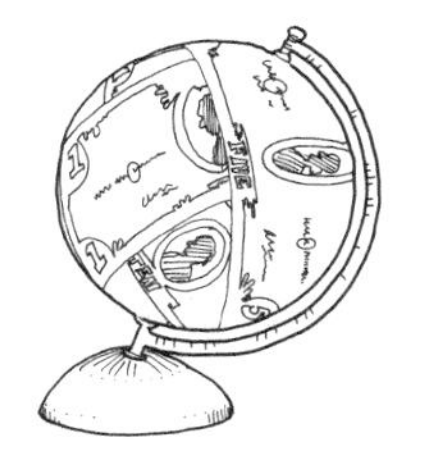

Geografía Económica

4 ¿Qué eventos podrían poner en peligro la economía del área?

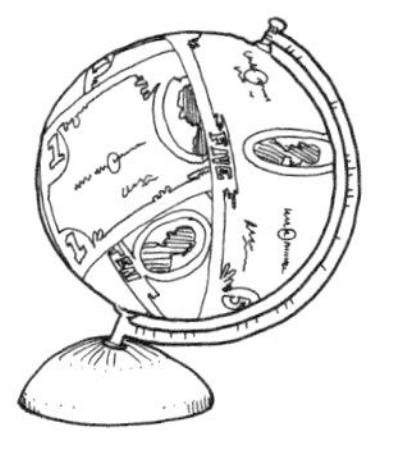

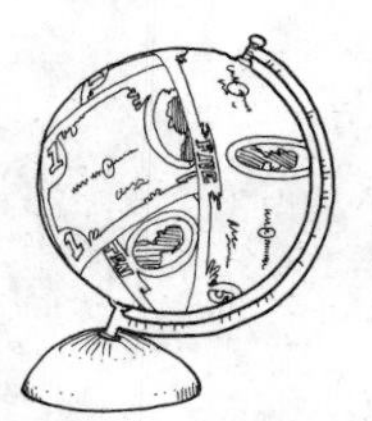

Geografía Económica
Question Cards

Geografía Económica

5 ¿Cómo podría cambiar la economía del área en los próximos 100 años?

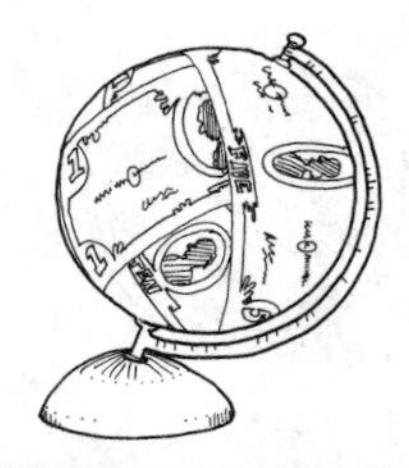

Geografía Económica

6 Explica cómo la ubicación del área pudo haber influido en su crecimiento económico.

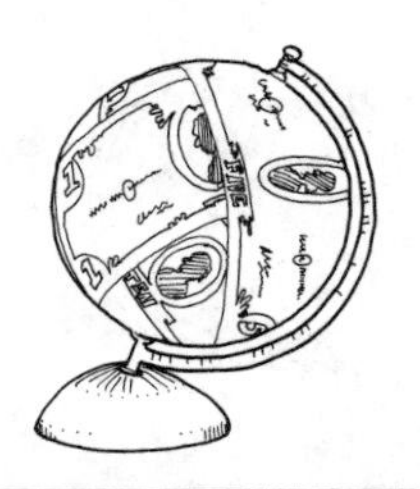

Geografía Económica

7 ¿Es el área un centro comercial importante? Explica tu respuesta.

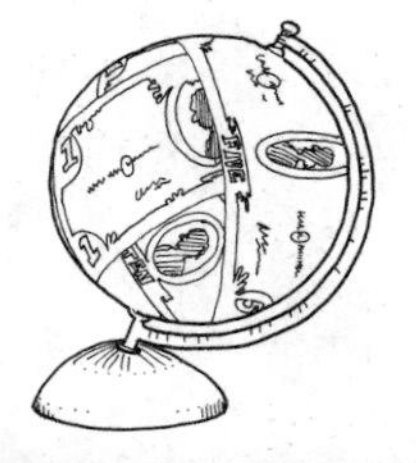

Geografía Económica

8 ¿Qué diría un economista acerca del área?

Geografía Económica
Question Cards

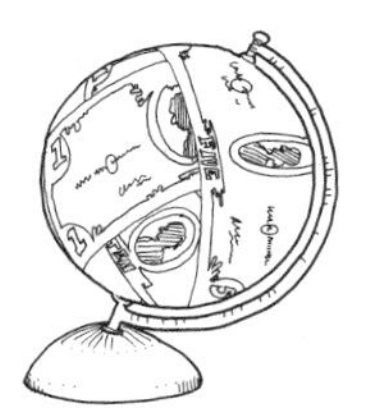

Geografía Económica

9 ¿Qué puedes decir acerca de la tierra del área?

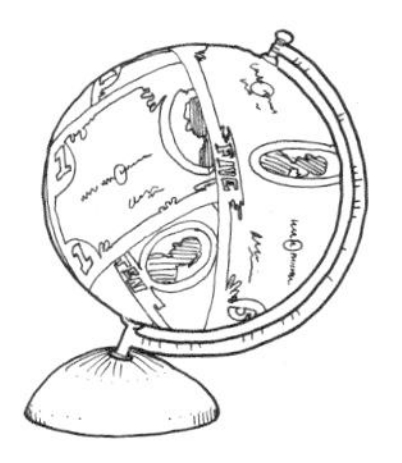

Geografía Económica

10 ¿Qué herramientas pudo haber usado la antigua cultura del área?

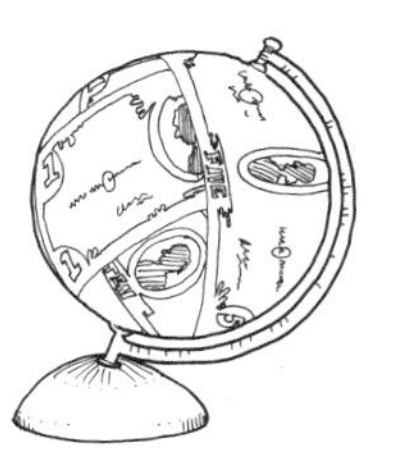

Geografía Económica

11 ¿Cómo el hecho de estar cerca, o lejos, de una fuente de agua puede afectar la economía de un área?

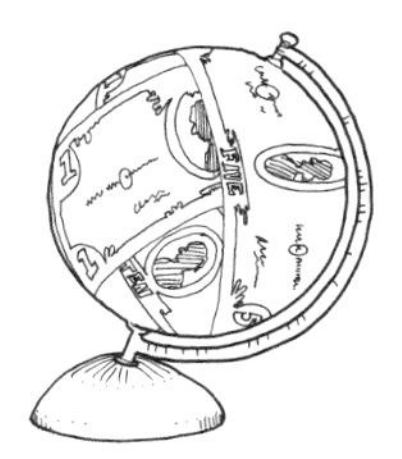

Geografía Económica

12 ¿Qué clase de tecnología podría mejorar la economía del área?

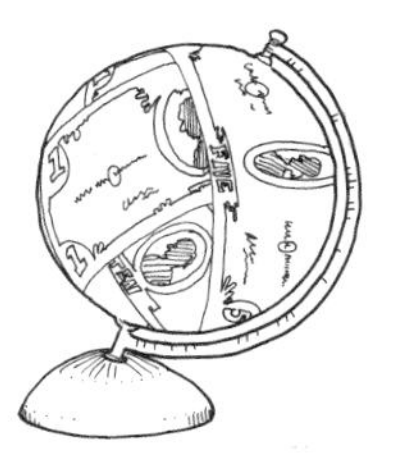

Geografía Económica
Question Cards

Geografía Económica

13 ¿De qué forma la ubicación del área permitía el trueque y el comercio?

Geografía Económica

14 ¿Cómo se vería afectada la economía del área si se agotaran los recursos naturales?

Geografía Económica

15 ¿Cómo han afectado las comunicaciones con otras áreas el crecimiento económico del área?

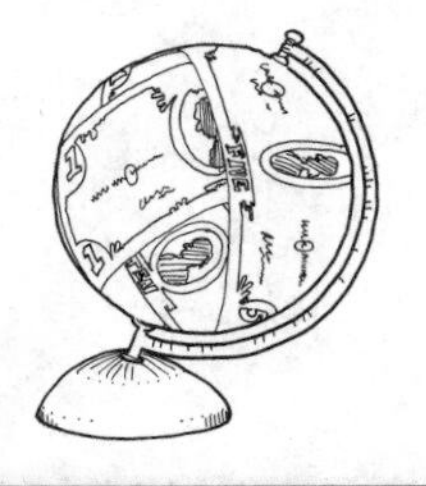

Geografía Económica

16 ¿Qué aptitudes necesitaría una persona para trabajar en el área?

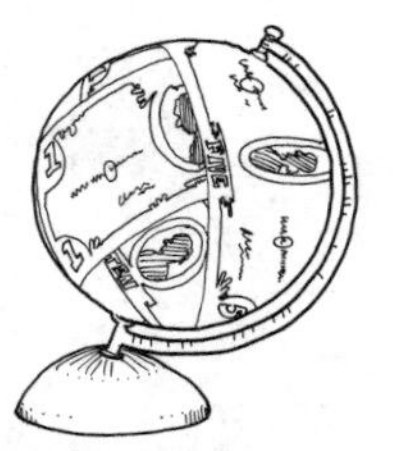

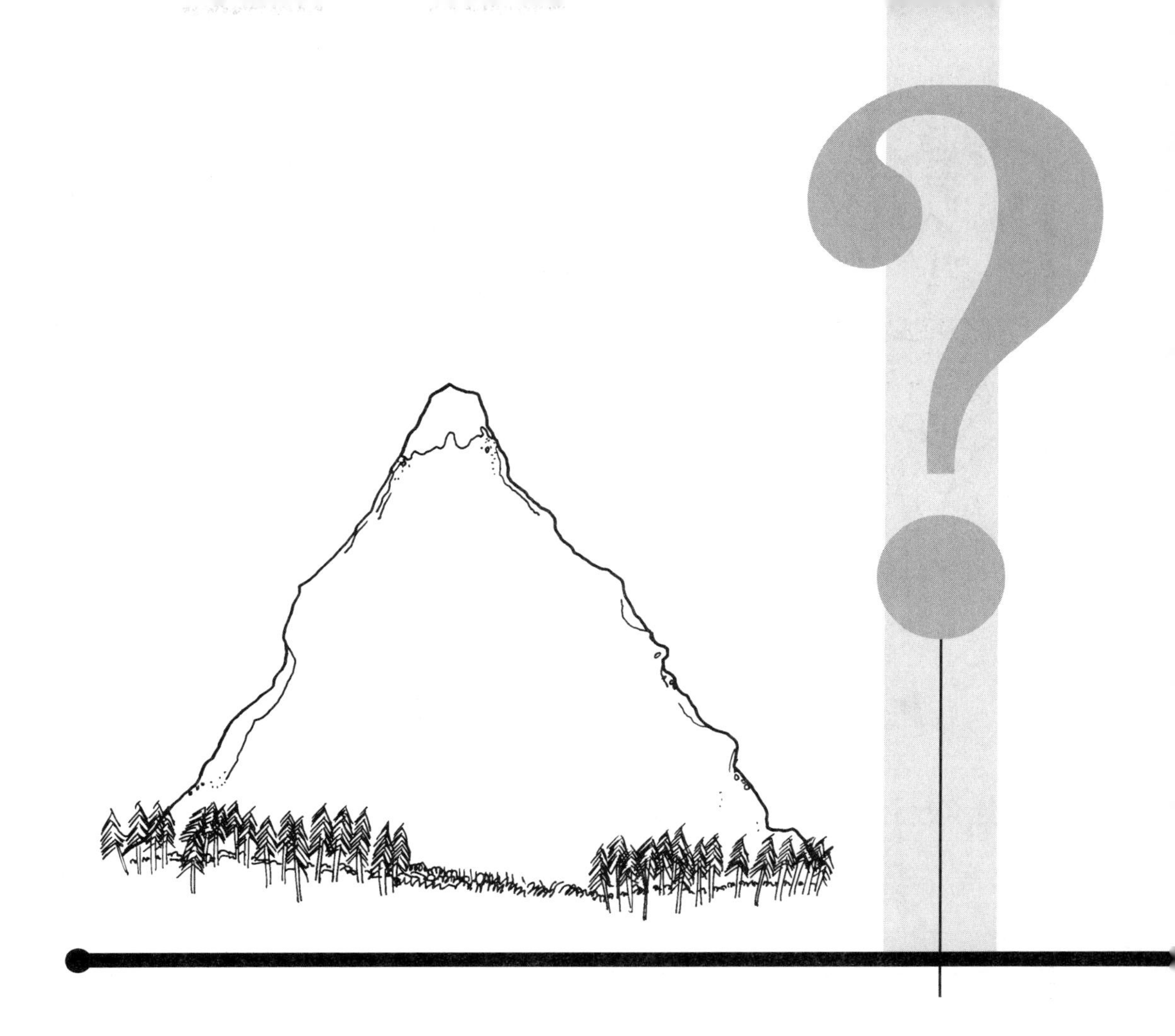

Geografía Física

Geography: Physical

higher-level thinking questions

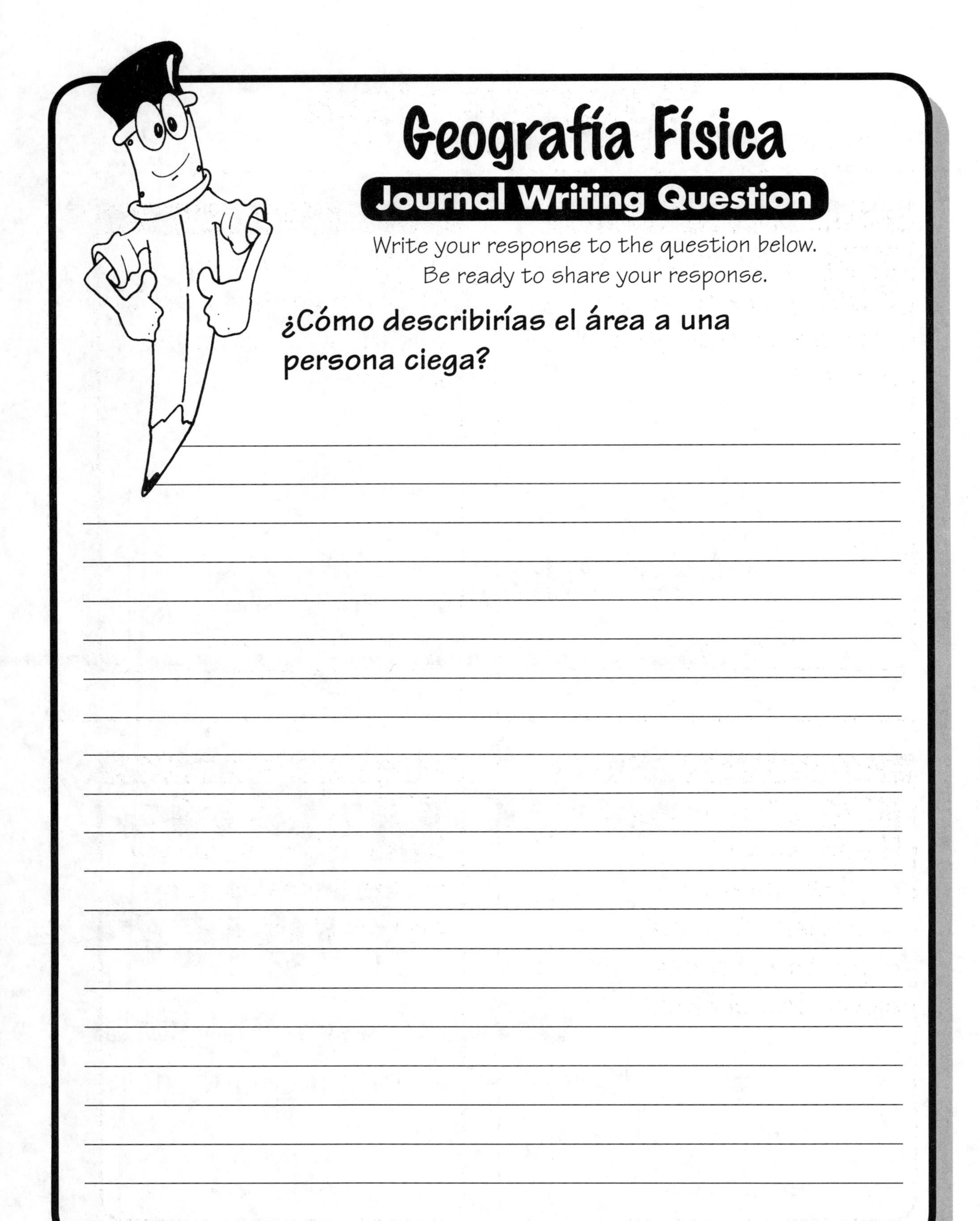

Geografía Física

Journal Writing Question

Write your response to the question below.
Be ready to share your response.

¿Cómo describirías el área a una persona ciega?

Geografía Física
Question Cards

Geografía Física

1 ¿Qué medios de transporte son más adecuados para el área?

Geografía Física

2 Describe un paisaje del área que pudiera pintar un artista.

Geografía Física

3 ¿Por qué podrías encontrar caparazones de animales marinos en el punto de mayor elevación del área?

Geografía Física

4 ¿En qué sería diferente la vida sin los animales que viven en el área?

Geografía Física
Question Cards

Geografía Física

5 ¿Qué información podrías dar para describir la ubicación exacta del área en el mapa?

Geografía Física

6 ¿Cómo se han adaptado los habitantes del área a las condiciones físicas externas?

Geografía Física

7 Elige una palabra que describa el clima del área.

Geografía Física

8 ¿Cómo se han adaptado las plantas del área a vivir allí?

Geografía Física
Question Cards

Geografía Física

9 Algunos científicos creen que antiguamente había un solo continente grande en la Tierra. ¿Qué países actuales podrían haber bordeado el área?

Geografía Física

10 ¿Cómo han afectado los desastres naturales al área?

Geografía Física

11 ¿Qué clase de desastres naturales se producen en el área? ¿Por qué?

Geografía Física

12 ¿Qué otras áreas tienen accidentes geográficos similares?

Geografía Física
Question Cards

Geografía Física

13 ¿Cómo describirías el área a una persona ciega?

Geografía Física

14 ¿Es el área más horizontal o vertical?

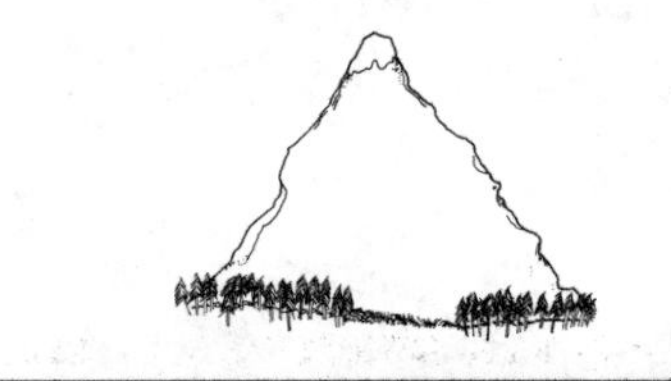

Geografía Física

15 ¿Cómo afecta al clima del área la distancia que la separa del ecuador?

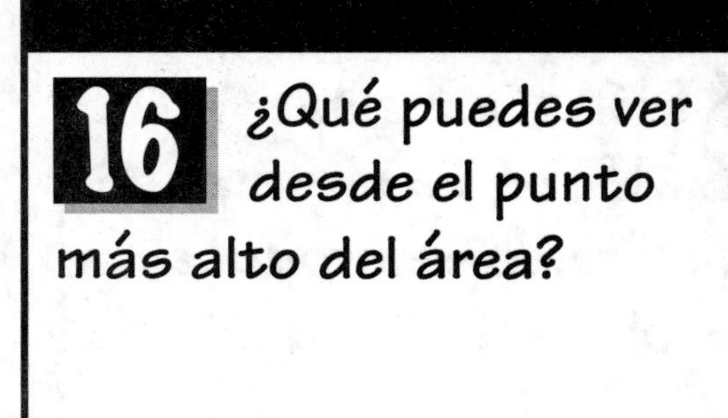

16 ¿Qué puedes ver desde el punto más alto del área?

Personaje Histórico

Historical Character

higher-level thinking questions

Personaje Histórico

Journal Writing Question

Write your response to the question below.
Be ready to share your response.

¿En qué sería diferente el mundo de hoy si este personaje no hubiera existido?

Personaje Histórico
Question Cards

Personaje Histórico

1 Si el personaje estuviera vivo, ¿qué podría lograr hoy en día?

Personaje Histórico

2 ¿En qué se parece a ti este personaje? ¿En qué se diferencia de ti?

Personaje Histórico

3 Este personaje ha regresado para visitar al presidente de los Estados Unidos. ¿Qué consejo le podría dar el personaje al Presidente?

Personaje Histórico

4 ¿En qué sería diferente el mundo de hoy si este personaje no hubiera existido?

Personaje Histórico
Question Cards

Personaje Histórico

5 Nuestras acciones revelan nuestros valores. ¿Cuál es el valor más importante que reflejan las acciones de esta persona?

Personaje Histórico

6 Considera los logros de este personaje. Si tú fueras este personaje, ¿de qué logros te sentirías más orgulloso?

Personaje Histórico

7 Si pudieras hacer dos preguntas a este personaje, ¿qué le preguntarías?

Personaje Histórico

8 A esta persona le han concedido tres deseos para cambiar el mundo de hoy. ¿Cuáles pueden ser sus deseos?

Personaje Histórico
Question Cards

Personaje Histórico

9 Si hubiera una acción de esta persona que pudieras cambiar, ¿cuál sería? ¿Por qué?

Personaje Histórico

10 Describe los rasgos físicos de esta persona. Si pudieras cambiar uno, ¿cuál cambiarías? ¿Por qué?

Personaje Histórico

11 Si el personaje saliera de vacaciones por dos semanas, ¿adónde iría y por qué?

Personaje Histórico

12 Te han concedido un día para viajar al pasado y adquirir la identidad de esta persona. ¿Qué harías de forma diferente?

Personaje Histórico
Question Cards

Personaje Histórico

13 Imagínate que se transporta a esta persona a la segunda Guerra Mundial. ¿Qué papel desempeñaría?

Personaje Histórico

14 Esta persona está sola en su casa, escribiendo en un diario. Comienza a escribir: "Lo que más me molesta es..." Completa la idea y explica por qué.

Personaje Histórico

15 Te han concedido poderes especiales que te hacen invisible y te permiten viajar al pasado. ¿Qué acontecimiento de la vida del personaje te gustaría observar?

Personaje Histórico

16 Has abierto una carta escrita al mejor amigo del personaje. La carta dice: "Lo que más siento es..." Completa la oración.

Eventos Históricos

Historical Events

higher-level thinking questions

Eventos Históricos

Journal Writing Question

Write your response to the question below.
Be ready to share your response.

Imagínate que formas parte de este evento. ¿Qué información incluirías en una carta que escribieras a tu casa?

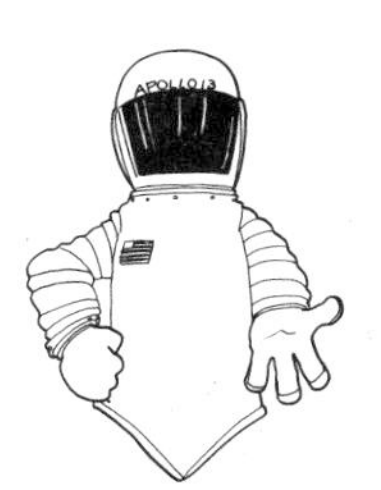

Eventos Históricos
Question Cards

Eventos Históricos

1 Explica la situación inmediatamente anterior a este evento.

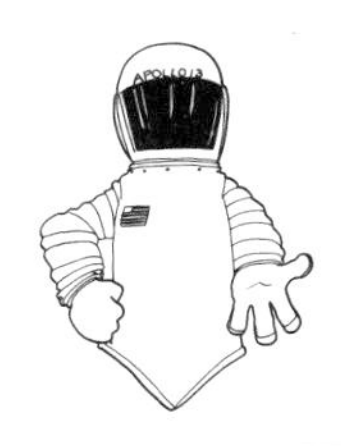

Eventos Históricos

2 Explica la situación inmediatamente posterior a este evento.

Eventos Históricos

3 ¿Qué efecto tuvo este evento en la historia del mundo?

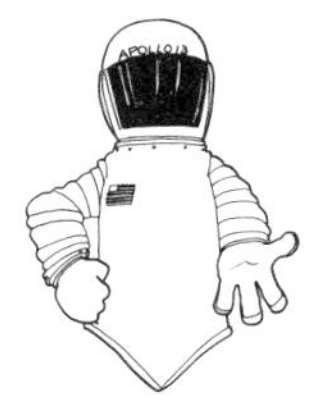

Eventos Históricos

4 ¿De qué forma hubiera sido diferente este evento si hubiera ocurrido en la actualidad?

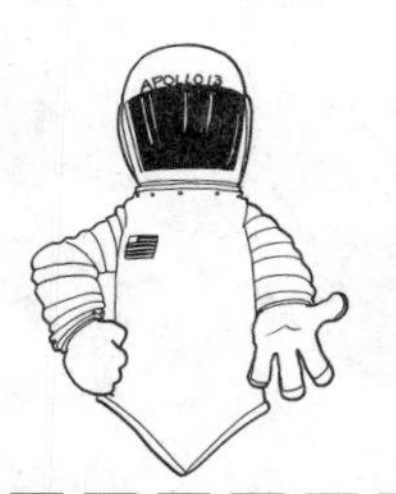

Eventos Históricos
Question Cards

Eventos Históricos

5 ¿Te hubiera gustado haber formado parte de este evento? ¿Por qué?

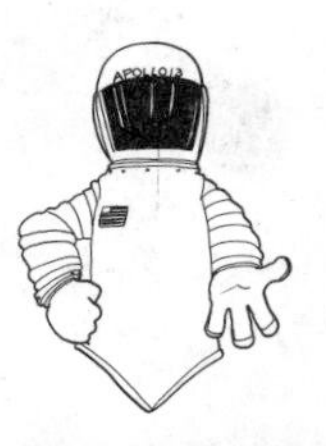

Eventos Históricos

6 Imagínate que eras un reportero encargado de cubrir este evento. Describe lo que hubieras podido ver y oír.

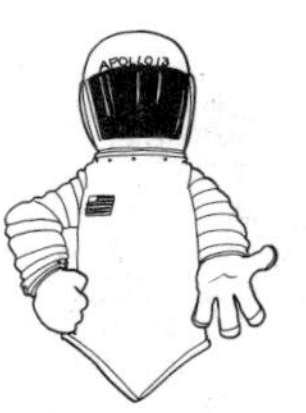

Eventos Históricos

7 Imagínate que hubiera salido una fotografía del evento en el periódico. ¿Qué diría el pie de fotografía?

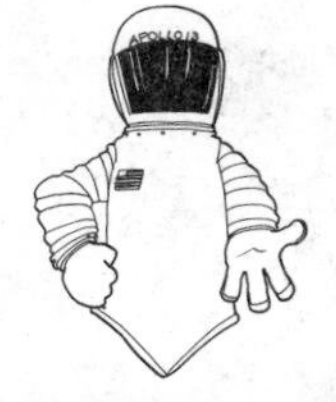

Eventos Históricos

8 Imagina que se fuera a levantar un monumento en memoria de este evento histórico. ¿Qué aspecto tendría y por qué?

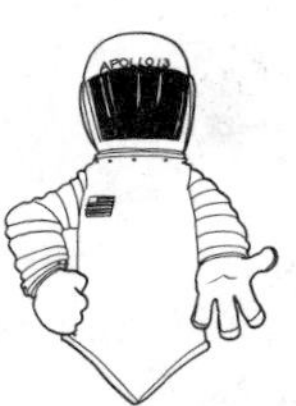

Eventos Históricos

Question Cards

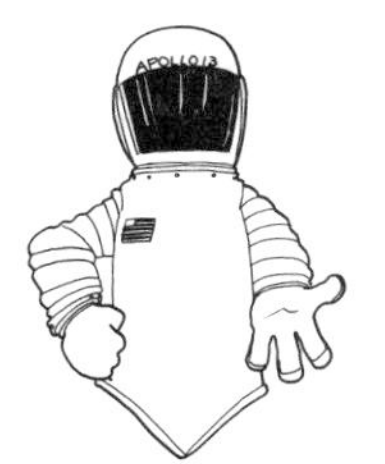

Eventos Históricos

9 ¿Cuáles fueron las personas más importantes implicadas en el evento?

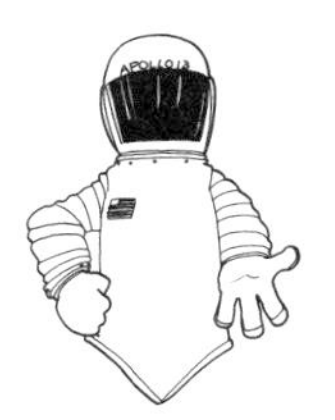

Eventos Históricos

10 Si se contratara a un artista para pintar una escena del evento, ¿qué escena debería pintar el artista que representara mejor el evento?

Eventos Históricos

11 Si pudieras cambiar una parte de este evento, o todo, ¿qué cambiarías y por qué?

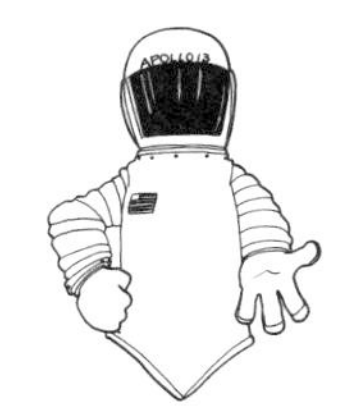

Eventos Históricos

12 ¿Qué hubiera podido suceder para cambiar el desenlace del evento?

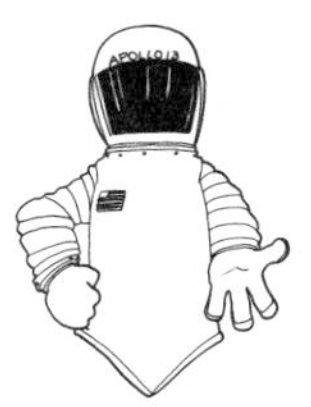

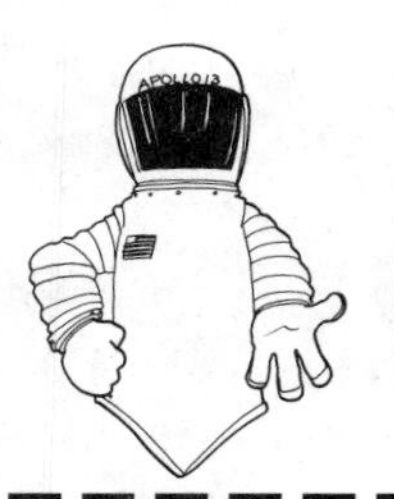

Eventos Históricos
Question Cards

Eventos Históricos

13 Imagínate que formas parte de este evento. ¿Qué información incluirías en una carta que escribieras a tu casa?

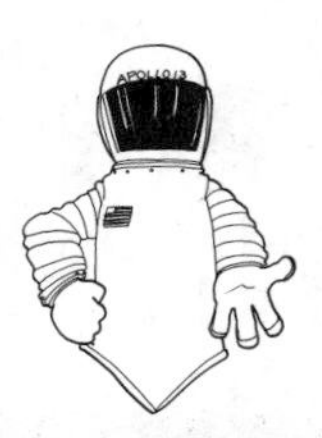

Eventos Históricos

14 Imagina que se hace una película sobre este evento. ¿Sería una película cómica, dramática, de acción/aventuras o de miedo?

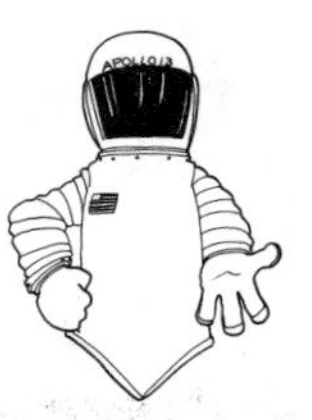

Eventos Históricos

15 ¿Qué efectos han tenido sobre tu vida y la de tu familia, las consecuencias de este evento?

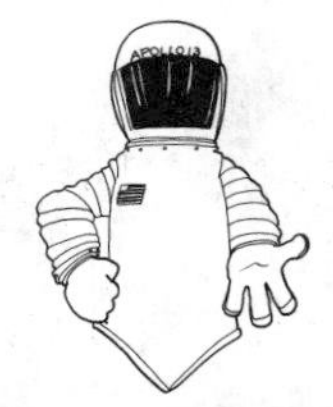

Eventos Históricos

16 ¿Cómo hubiera afectado al evento un cambio meteorológico?

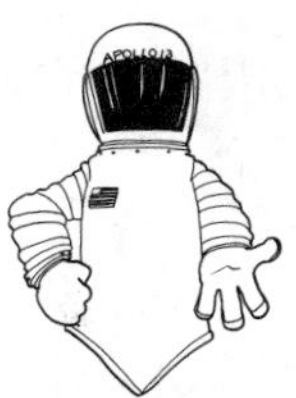

Especies en Peligro de Extinción

Endangered Species

higher-level thinking questions

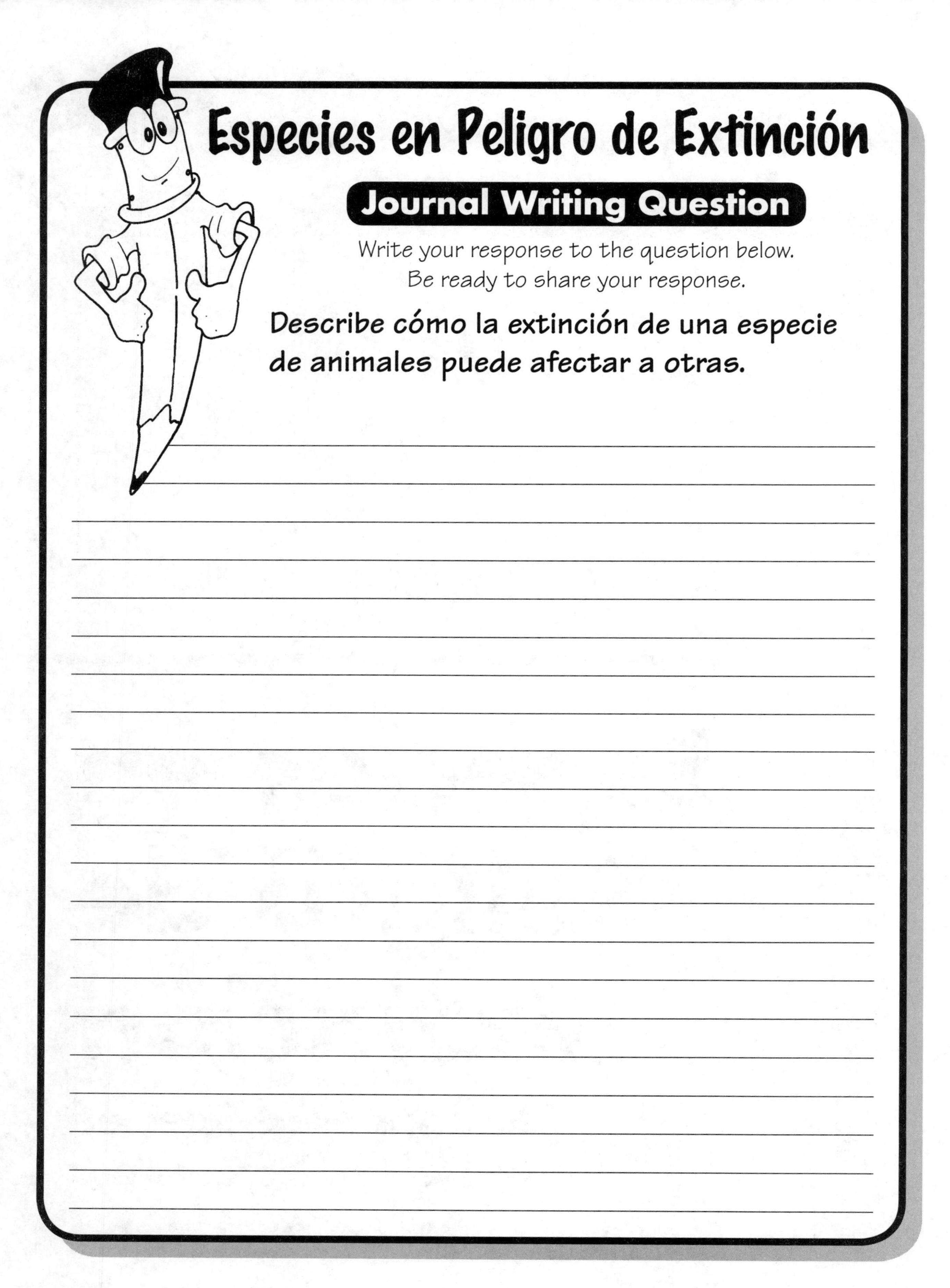

Especies en Peligro de Extinción

Journal Writing Question

Write your response to the question below.
Be ready to share your response.

Describe cómo la extinción de una especie de animales puede afectar a otras.

Especies en Peligro de Extinción

Question Cards

Especies en Peligro de Extinción

1 ¿De qué forma la economía de un lugar pone en peligro de extinción a sus animales?

Especies en Peligro de Extinción

2 ¿Qué puede hacer la gente para proteger a las especies en peligro de extinción que viven en su área o en otros continentes?

Especies en Peligro de Extinción

3 Si se siguen destruyendo las selvas tropicales, ¿cuáles serán los posibles efectos en todo el mundo?

Especies en Peligro de Extinción

4 El uso de insecticidas afecta a la población de aves. ¿Cómo afecta esto, a su vez, a la población humana?

Especies en Peligro de Extinción

Question Cards

Especies en Peligro de Extinción

5 Evalúa la necesidad de obtener madera comparándola con la necesidad de conservar el hábitat del búho moteado.

Especies en Peligro de Extinción

6 ¿Por qué se permite la caza controlada cuando hay tantos animales en peligro de extinción y extintos?

Especies en Peligro de Extinción

7 ¿Qué podría inventarse en el futuro para proteger a las especies en peligro de extinción?

Especies en Peligro de Extinción

8 Elige una especie en peligro de extinción y enumera tantas formas como puedas para ayudar a protegerla.

Especies en Peligro de Extinción
Question Cards

Especies en Peligro de Extinción

9 Imagínate que eres el director de una nueva revista sobre animales en peligro de extinción. ¿Qué escogerías para la noticia de primera página y por qué?

Especies en Peligro de Extinción

10 ¿Como afecta a los animales el aumento de la población en la Tierra?

Especies en Peligro de Extinción

11 ¿Cómo han ayudado los medios de comunicación (TV, películas) a educarnos acerca de nuestras especies en peligro de extinción?

Especies en Peligro de Extinción

12 Describe cómo la extinción de una especie de animales puede afectar a otras.

Especies en Peligro de Extinción
Question Cards

Especies en Peligro de Extinción

13 Como funcionario del gobierno tienes que decidir cómo se deben emplear 1,000,000 de dólares. ¿Qué parte de este dinero deberá emplearse en la protección de los hábitats de los animales locales?

Especies en Peligro de Extinción

14 ¿Debería permitirse que continuara la perforación y el transporte de petróleo en el mar? ¿Por qué?

Especies en Peligro de Extinción

15 Si pudieras regresar a la vida a una especie extinta, ¿qué especie sería y por qué?

Especies en Peligro de Extinción

16 Estás escribiendo una carta al periódico acerca de un sistema de transporte de alta tecnología que han planeado para tu área. Proporcionará puestos de trabajo y dinero de impuestos a tu comunidad y destruirá el hábitat de un insecto diminuto. ¿Qué dirás en tu carta?

Cómo Investigar los Inventos

Investigating Invention

higher-level thinking questions

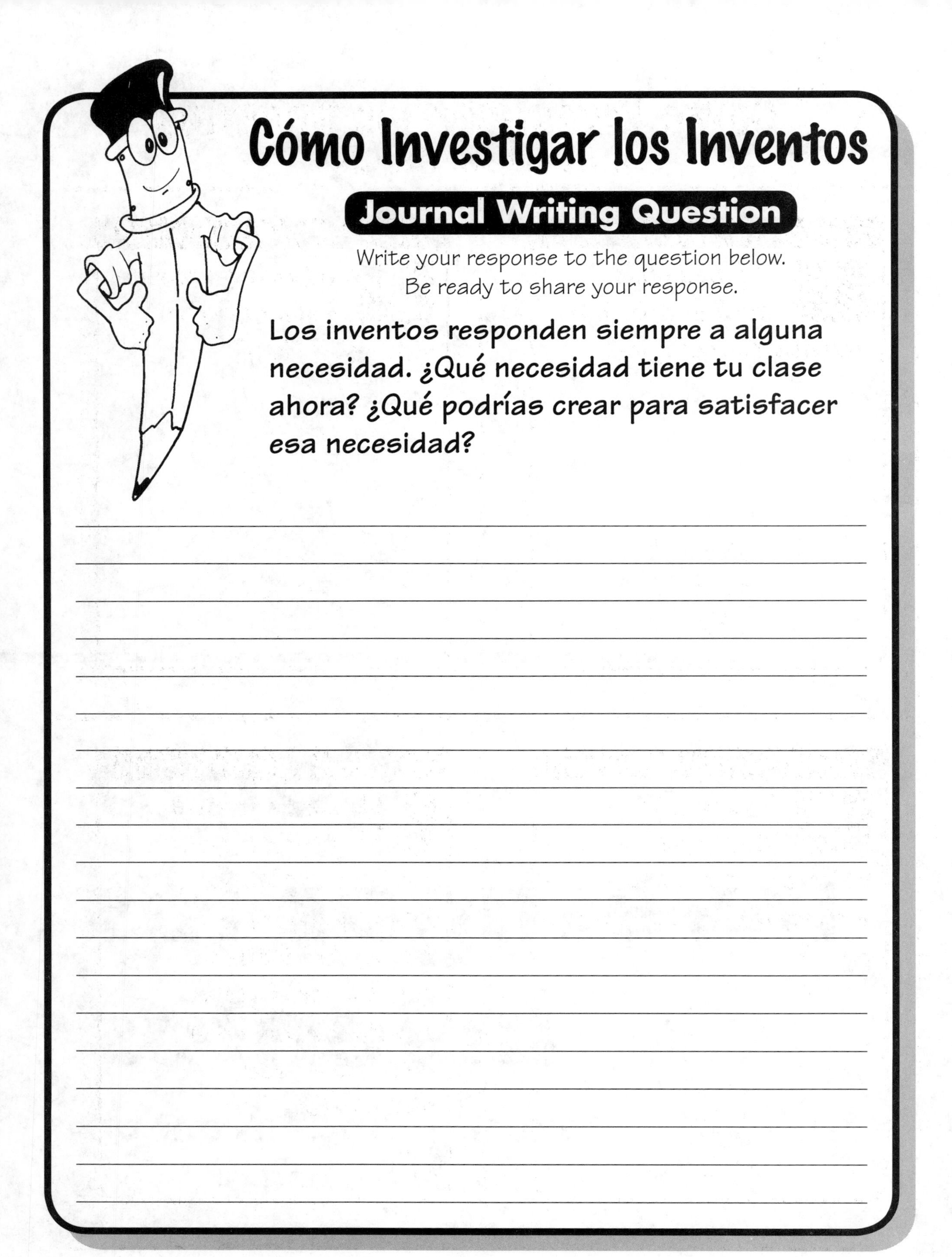

Cómo Investigar los Inventos

Journal Writing Question

Write your response to the question below.
Be ready to share your response.

Los inventos responden siempre a alguna necesidad. ¿Qué necesidad tiene tu clase ahora? ¿Qué podrías crear para satisfacer esa necesidad?

Cómo Investigar los Inventos

Question Cards

Cómo Investigar los Inventos

1 Predice cuál será el próximo invento tecnológico.

Cómo Investigar los Inventos

2 ¿Qué inventarías para hacer tu vida más fácil?

Cómo Investigar los Inventos

3 Imagina la vida antes de haberse inventado el automóvil. ¿Era mejor o peor?

Cómo Investigar los Inventos

4 Los inventos responden siempre a alguna necesidad. ¿Qué necesidad tiene tu clase ahora? ¿Qué podrías crear para satisfacer esa necesidad?

Cómo Investigar los Inventos

Question Cards

Cómo Investigar los Inventos

5 ¿En qué sería diferente tu vida sin la invención del reloj?

Cómo Investigar los Inventos

6 Escoge un invento reciente y evalúa su utilidad.

Cómo Investigar los Inventos

7 ¿Crees que el descubrimiento de la energía nuclear fue una contribución positiva para el mundo? ¿Por qué?

Cómo Investigar los Inventos

8 ¿Qué características debe tener un inventor?

Cómo Investigar los Inventos

Question Cards

Cómo Investigar los Inventos

9 ¿Consideras que una nueva receta es una invención? ¿Por qué?

Cómo Investigar los Inventos

10 Escoge una invención en tu casa y explica en qué sería diferente la vida sin ella.

Cómo Investigar los Inventos

11 En tu opinión, ¿qué invento ha ocasionado más daños a la sociedad? ¿Por qué?

Cómo Investigar los Inventos

12 El teléfono ha progresado mucho desde la primera conversación telefónica. ¿Cómo serán las comunicaciones electrónicas dentro de 100 años?

Cómo Investigar los Inventos
Question Cards

Cómo Investigar los Inventos

13 Escoge un inventor que aprecies y explica por qué.

Cómo Investigar los Inventos

14 ¿Cómo afectó a la sociedad la invención de la computadora personal?

Cómo Investigar los Inventos

15 Nombra una invención creada en el siglo diecinueve y que siga siendo efectiva hoy. ¿Qué invención del siglo veinte seguirá siendo efectiva dentro de 100 años?

Cómo Investigar los Inventos

16 ¿Cuál ha sido la invención más importante de la historia?

Sistema Solar

Solar System

higher-level thinking questions

Sistema Solar

Journal Writing Question

Write your response to the question below.
Be ready to share your response.

Describe las características importantes que debe tener un astronauta.

Sistema Solar
Question Cards

Sistema Solar

1 Imagínate que te han escogido para vivir en la primera colonia espacial. ¿Cuáles tres artículos personales te gustaría llevar contigo y por qué?

Sistema Solar

2 ¿Crees que el dinero de los impuestos que se dedica a la exploración espacial está bien empleado?

Sistema Solar

3 ¿Has jugado alguna vez a la Rana Saltarina? ¿Qué relación tiene la Rana Saltarina con el uso de las estaciones espaciales?

Sistema Solar

4 Describe las características importantes que debe tener un astronauta.

Sistema Solar
Question Cards

Sistema Solar

5 ¿Serías un buen viajero espacial? ¿Por qué?

Sistema Solar

6 La mejor película del año 2050 se rodó en Neptuno. ¿Sobre qué trataba?

Sistema Solar

7 Piensa como una persona que vende bienes raíces. ¿Cómo le venderías una casa en Plutón a un cliente?

Sistema Solar

8 Imagínate que has aterrizado en Venus. ¿Qué verías?

Sistema Solar
Question Cards

Sistema Solar

9 Describe la casa perfecta para vivir en la Luna.

Sistema Solar

10 Decide en qué planeta puede existir vida y di por qué.

Sistema Solar

11 ¿Cuál debe ser nuestra próxima exploración espacial?

Sistema Solar

12 ¿Podrán vivir los seres humanos alguna vez en otro planeta? ¿Por qué?

Sistema Solar
Question Cards

Sistema Solar

13 Predice qué sucedería si aprendiéramos a viajar por el espacio a una mayor velocidad.

Sistema Solar

14 La exploración espacial conduce a muchos descubrimientos sorprendentes. Recientemente hemos aprendido a crear rodamientos, ropas ligeras y alimentos nutritivos duraderos perfectos — todos en el espacio. ¿Cuál será nuestro próximo “producto espacial”?

Sistema Solar

15 Acabas de ordenar un nuevo postre, “El Saturno”, en tu restaurante favorito. ¿Qué aspecto y que sabor tiene?

Sistema Solar

16 ¿Quiénes deberían formar parte de la tripulación del primer viaje tripulado a Marte?

Arte: Cómo Examinar un Dibujo

Art: Scanning a Print

higher-level thinking questions

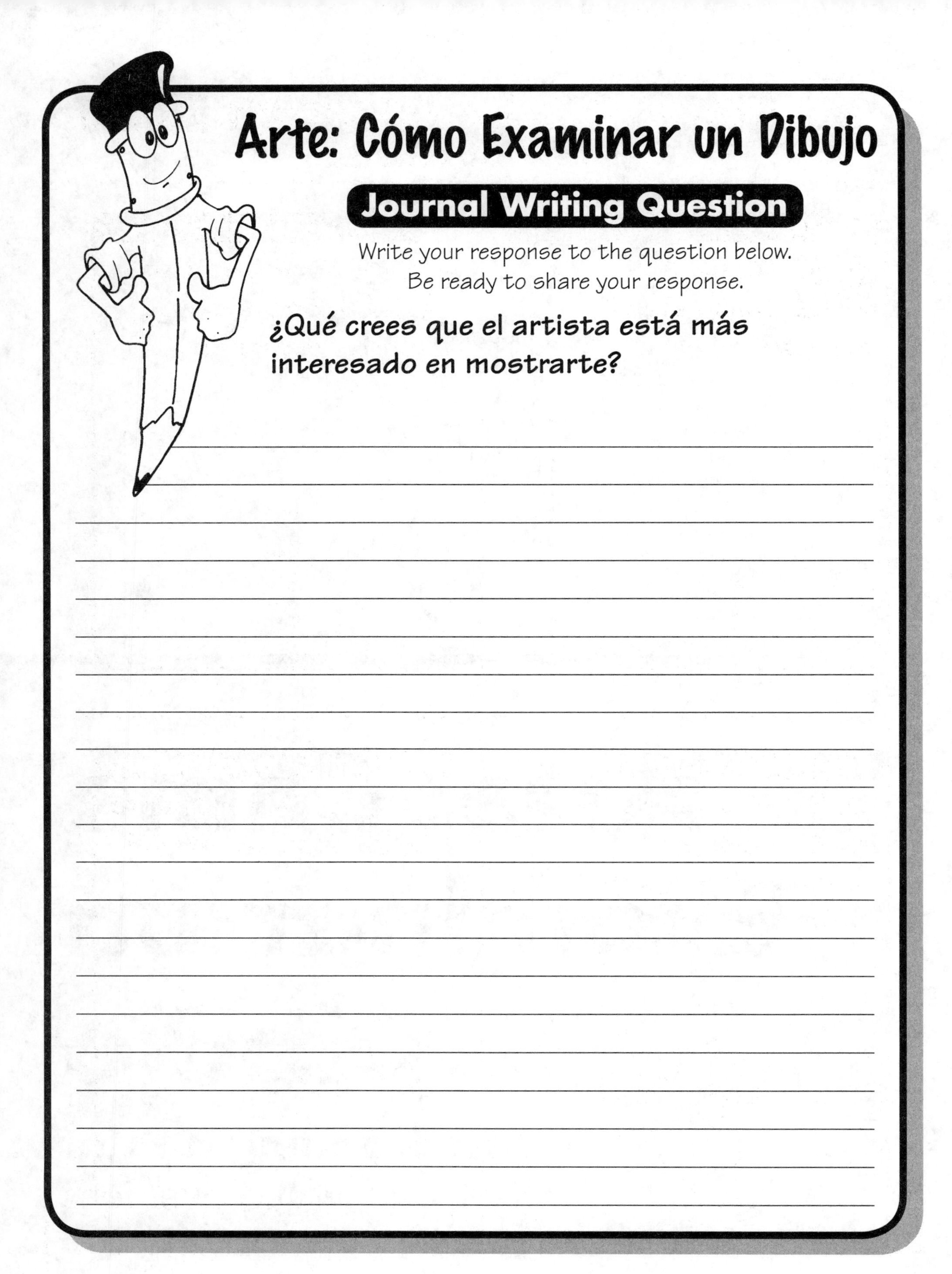

Arte: Cómo Examinar un Dibujo

Journal Writing Question

Write your response to the question below.
Be ready to share your response.

¿Qué crees que el artista está más interesado en mostrarte?

Arte: Cómo Examinar un Dibujo
Question Cards

Arte: Cómo Examinar un Dibujo

1 ¿Cómo usa el contraste el artista?

Arte: Cómo Examinar un Dibujo

2 Ponle un nuevo nombre a este dibujo y explica tu elección.

Arte: Cómo Examinar un Dibujo

3 Si se escribiera música basada en este dibujo, ¿qué instrumento se usaría?

Arte: Cómo Examinar un Dibujo

4 ¿Cuál es el punto focal del dibujo?

Arte: Cómo Examinar un Dibujo

Question Cards

Arte: Cómo Examinar un Dibujo

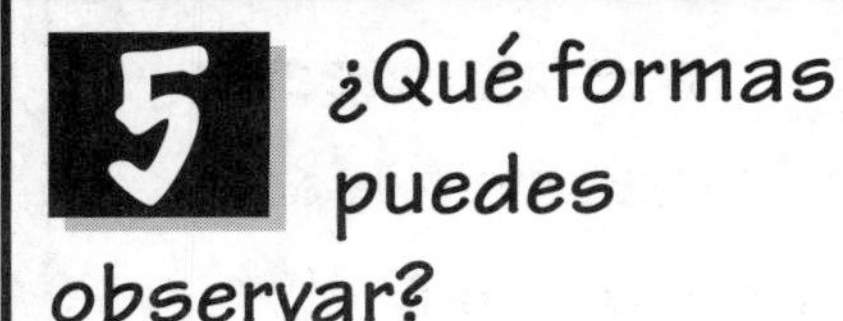

5 ¿Qué formas puedes observar?

Arte: Cómo Examinar un Dibujo

6 Si este dibujo fuera la portada de un libro, ¿qué clase de literatura sería?

Arte: Cómo Examinar un Dibujo

7 ¿Qué diferencias habría en el dibujo si fuera blanco y negro o en colores?

Arte: Cómo Examinar un Dibujo

8 ¿Qué sensaciones crean los colores?

Arte: Cómo Examinar un Dibujo

Question Cards

Arte: Cómo Examinar un Dibujo

9 Si esta pieza fuera una persona, ¿quién sería y por qué?

Arte: Cómo Examinar un Dibujo

10 ¿Qué puedes suponer acerca de un artista basándote en su obra?

Arte: Cómo Examinar un Dibujo

11 Imagínate que este dibujo es un anuncio. ¿Qué trataría de vender?

Arte: Cómo Examinar un Dibujo

12 ¿Qué parte del dibujo te produce la sensación de movimiento?

Arte: Cómo Examinar un Dibujo

Question Cards

Arte: Cómo Examinar un Dibujo

13 Elige cinco palabras de acción para describir el dibujo.

Arte: Cómo Examinar un Dibujo

14 ¿Qué crees que el artista está más interesado en mostrarte?

Arte: Cómo Examinar un Dibujo

15 ¿A quién incluirías en el dibujo y por qué?

Arte: Cómo Examinar un Dibujo

16 ¿Qué puedes aprender acerca del período de tiempo en el que fue creado el dibujo?

Elementos del Arte

Elements of Art

higher-level thinking questions

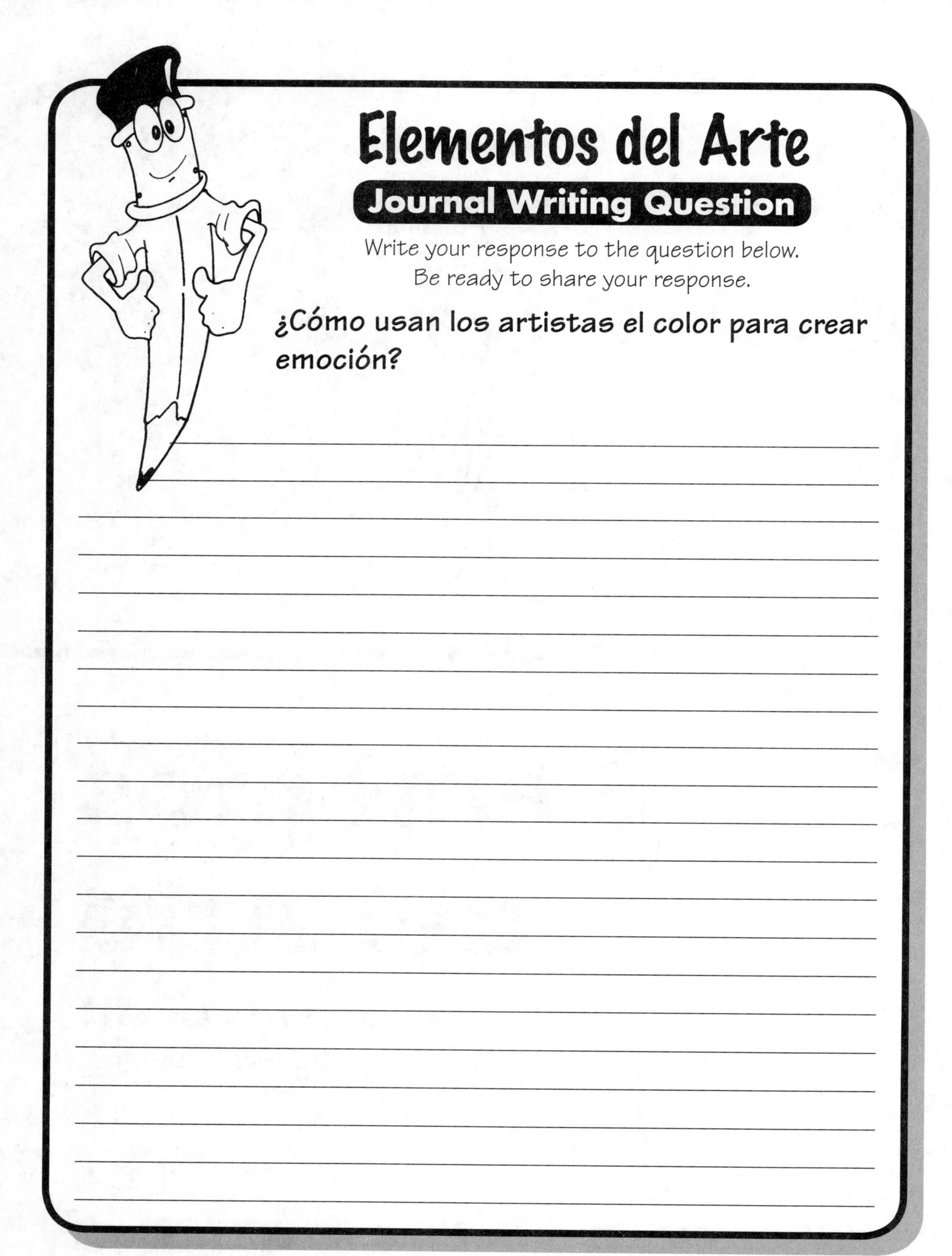

Elementos del Arte

Journal Writing Question

Write your response to the question below.
Be ready to share your response.

¿Cómo usan los artistas el color para crear emoción?

Elementos del Arte
Question Cards

Elementos del Arte

1 Imagínate que estás en el departamento de vegetales y frutas de una tienda de alimentos. ¿Cómo ha usado el tendero la forma para hacer el área más atractiva?

Elementos del Arte

2 Da un ejemplo de valor intrínseco en la naturaleza.

Elementos del Arte

3 ¿Cómo usan los artistas el color para crear emoción?

Elementos del Arte

4 ¿Cómo usan los grandes cocineros la textura para mejorar el aspecto de los platos que preparan?

Elementos del Arte
Question Cards

Elementos del Arte

5 ¿Qué elementos puedes encontrar a tu alrededor?

Elementos del Arte

6 ¿Qué elementos representan mejor tu personalidad: la dirección continua de una línea, la calidad variada de la textura o la profundidad de una forma?

Elementos del Arte

7 ¿Qué elementos se pueden ver tanto en las pirámides antiguas como en los rascacielos modernos?

Elementos del Arte

8 ¿Cómo describirías tu obra de arte favorita en lo que se refiere a sus elementos?

Elementos del Arte

Question Cards

Elementos del Arte

9 ¿Qué estación del año es más intensa en color? ¿Puedes ver más colores elementales o secundarios?

Elementos del Arte

10 Los animales son a menudo sujetos del arte. Si fueras a pintar un animal, ¿cuál pintarías y qué elemento destacarías?

Elementos del Arte

11 La publicidad impresa es una forma de arte. ¿Qué elementos se usan mucho en los anuncios de las revistas?

Elementos del Arte

12 Imagina tu carro favorito, haz una crítica de su apariencia usando los elementos.

Elementos del Arte
Question Cards

Elementos del Arte

13 Haz una descripción de tu compañero de equipo usando los elementos de color, forma y textura.

Elementos del Arte

14 Describe la forma de algo tuyo que te guste mucho. ¿Está abierto o cerrado, tiene forma cúbica o cónica? ¿Qué altura, anchura y profundidad tiene?

Elementos del Arte

15 Pon un ejemplo de espacio positivo en el mundo que te rodea.

Elementos del Arte

16 Pon un ejemplo de espacio negativo en el mundo que te rodea.

Apreciación de la Música

Music Appreciation

higher-level thinking questions

Apreciación de la Música

Journal Writing Question

Write your response to the question below.
Be ready to share your response.

Si esta música fuera el tema de una película, ¿de qué trataría la película?

Apreciación de la Música

Question Cards

Apreciación de la Música

1 Describe el movimiento de la música.

Apreciación de la Música

2 Si esta música fuera el tema de una película, ¿de qué trataría la película?

Apreciación de la Música

3 ¿Cómo crees que se sentía el compositor cuando escribió esta música?

Apreciación de la Música

4 ¿Qué instrumentos puedes oír?

Apreciación de la Música
Question Cards

Apreciación de la Música

5 ¿Qué instrumentos podrías incluir para cambiar esta música?

Apreciación de la Música

6 ¿Qué sonidos de la naturaleza puedes oír en esta música?

Apreciación de la Música

7 Si la música se usara en un anuncio de televisión, ¿qué vendería el anunciante?

Apreciación de la Música

8 Pon un nuevo título a la música y explica tu elección.

Apreciación de la Música

Question Cards

Apreciación de la Música

9 Si esta música tuviera sabor, ¿a qué sabría?

Apreciación de la Música

10 ¿Qué estación del año representa mejor esta música?

Apreciación de la Música

11 ¿Qué evento o experiencia podría haber inspirado esta música?

Apreciación de la Música

12 ¿Cómo quiere el compositor que se sientan los oyentes?

Apreciación de la Música
Question Cards

Apreciación de la Música

13 Si tuvieras que pintar esta música, ¿qué aspecto tendría la pintura?

Apreciación de la Música

14 ¿Qué te apetece hacer cuando oyes esta música?

Apreciación de la Música

15 Si pudieras escribirle una carta al compositor, ¿qué le dirías?

Apreciación de la Música

16 ¿Qué crees que le gusta hacer al compositor en su tiempo libre?

Light the Fires of Your Students' Minds with this Terrific Series of Higher-Level Thinking Question Books!

Promote Non-Stop Discussion

Sharpen Thinking Skills

Improve Writing Skills

Loaded with Hundreds of Provocative, Intriguing, Mind-Stretching Questions and Activities!

KAGAN PUBLISHING

www.KaganOnline.com ★ 1(800) 933-2667

Kagan is your source for active engagement in the classroom.

Check out Kagan's line of books, smartcards, software, electronics, and hands-on learning resources all designed to boost engagement in your classroom.

Books

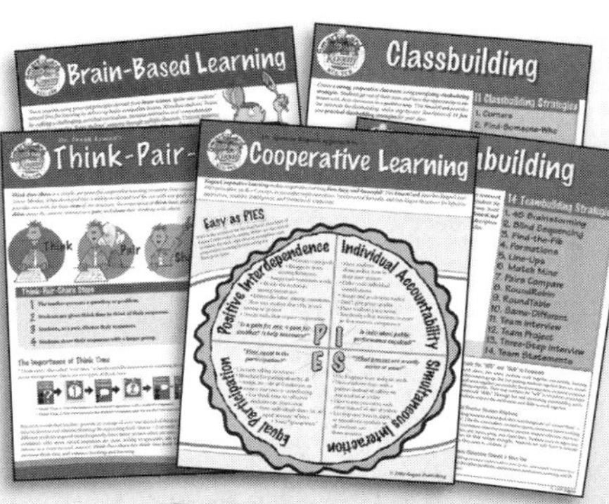

SmartCards

Spinners

Learning Chips

Posters

Learning Cubes

KAGAN PUBLISHING

www.KaganOnline.com ★ 1(800) 933-2667

Kagan is the world leader in creating active engagement in the classroom. Learn how to engage your students and you will boost achievement, prevent discipline problems, and make learning more fun and meaningful. Come join Kagan for a workshop or call Kagan to **set up a workshop for your school or district**. Experience the power of a Kagan workshop. **Experience the engagement!**

SPECIALIZING IN:

- ★ Cooperative Learning
- ★ Win-Win Discipline
- ★ Brain-Friendly Teaching
- ★ Multiple Intelligences
- ★ Thinking Skills
- ★ Kagan Coaching

KAGAN PROFESSIONAL DEVELOPMENT

www.KaganOnline.com ★ 1(800) 266-7576